PUFFIN BOOKS

Goalkeepers are Different

'A goalkeeper is nothing like as glamorous as a forward,' says Ronnie Blake, the rising young goalkeeper who describes his career in this book. Realism is the keynote of the story, which is so readable that it will enthral every football fan; and even if you're not interested in the game you will certainly see a lot more in it by the time you put the book down.

Brian Glanville is a novelist and sports journalist who really knows his subject from the inside, and the result is a fascinating glimpse into the world of the professional from early days as a club apprentice to the exhilarating heights at the top of the tree. Through Ronnie's experience the reader is given a real insight into the concern which injuries or loss of form can cause: Ronnie goes through one bad patch, when he starts losing his nerve and his whole team starts playing badly because of difficulties with their manager. But we learn too of the tremendous thrill of playing well, pitting oneself against the great names of football, perhaps even in a Cup final.

This is a book as gripping and fast-moving as a good football game.

Brian Glanville

Goalkeepers
are Different

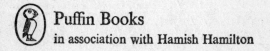
Puffin Books
in association with Hamish Hamilton

PUFFIN BOOKS

Published by the Penguin Group
27 Wrights Lane, London W8 5TZ, England
Viking Penguin Inc., 40 West 23rd Street, New York, New York 10010, USA
Penguin Books Australia Ltd, Ringwood, Victoria, Australia
Penguin Books Canada Ltd, 2801 John Street, Markham, Ontario, Canada L3R 1B4
Penguin Books (NZ) Ltd, 182–190 Wairau Road, Auckland 10, New Zealand

Penguin Books Ltd, Registered Offices: Harmondsworth, Middlesex, England

First published by Hamish Hamilton 1971
Published in Puffin Books 1974
10

Made and printed in Great Britain by
Richard Clay Ltd, Bungay, Suffolk
Set in Linotype Times

For Mark and Toby

Chapter 1

Some people say goalkeepers are crazy, but to me they're not crazy, they're different. A goalkeeper's on his own, in every way. First: he's the only one allowed to use his hands. Second, which people never seem to think of, he's alone there in his goal for most of the game. Of course there'll be a couple of full-backs on the line at corners, or under heavy pressure, but even when his team's taking a hammering, how much of the play is actually *round* the goal, how often is it in the penalty area, let alone the six-yard box? Very, very seldom, really. To me, football is a midfield game. It's like what people tell you who fought in the Great War, my grandfather and that; it's mostly fought in No Man's Land.

So most of the time there you are, alone on your line, pacing about, watching things, waiting for something to happen. They get a lot of time to think, goalkeepers. Too much, if you ask me. In fact, as far as I'm concerned, the more that's happening the better, because you can't make the saves unless you get the shots, and the more shots you get, the more saves you make, the more confident you are. Whereas the thing I hate, that every goalkeeper hates, is to be left there cold for half an hour while all the play's up at the other end, then away they come and out of the blue, bang, you've got to make a save, when you maybe haven't touched the ball for all that time. The worst thing of all, it may be a goal, and then you could have another twenty minutes to brood about it, while the play goes up the other end, again.

Picking the ball out of the net. That's the most terrible thing of the lot. In fact you may have noticed I avoid doing

7

it if I possibly can, I try to leave it to my full-backs. It's a habit I started at school, maybe even a superstition in a way, like my always, always putting my right boot on first, and being last but one down the tunnel, out on to the field. Now I'm established as the first team keeper, the boys respect it, they'll go into the net and fish the ball out for me, but before that I'd go to any sort of lengths not to do it; I'd lie there in the mud and not look behind me even, as if it hadn't happened, till somebody went in and booted it up-field again.

Away grounds are the worst, of course. When you're at home it's not quite so bad, because the crowd's with you; if you have to go into the net, after a goal, you'll hear them say, 'Hard luck, Ronnie; never mind, Ron.' But away, they're gloating, you see them through the netting, grinning at you, jigging up and down, making signs, till you wish you could pick up the ball and kick it at them.

That's the other thing about being on your own; you're not entirely on your own, because the crowd's there, too. It took a lot of getting used to, at first, coming out of the reserve team where there might be just a sprinkling of people on the terraces, to games where they might be packed in so tight they'd be swaying down the terraces like an avalanche, or something; I'd watch it down the other end of the field. Outfield players say, 'I don't take any notice of the crowds,' but it's all right for them, they're running about all the time, they never stay in one spot, and anyhow the only time they're near the crowd is when they come close to the touchlines. But a goalkeeper's got no choice; he's confined to his goal, and away from home it can be nasty at times, the abuse, and now and then the throwing things – as you'll see.

People ask, especially boys, how did you start, have you always been a goalkeeper, and my answer is that I became a goalkeeper by accident, like so many have. Because what does a boy want to be when he starts, who does he want to copy? He wants to be Geoff Hurst, banging in three in a World Cup Final. He wants to be Ron Davies, jumping five miles up and heading them in. Above anyone, he probably wants to be Georgie Best, wearing his hair long, dribbling past four or five men at a time, or scoring goals you'd never dream of till he's got them.

For me, as a Chelsea fan, the player I wanted to be when I was nine or ten was Jimmy Greaves; we all did. It was just before he went to Italy, then came back and played for Spurs, and nearly everybody in my school, in Notting Hill, was Jimmy in the playground. Those little, short legs, twinkling away, the sidesteps, the goals he made out of nothing, the long runs he used to go on, then – besides him being so young, and a London boy, as well. Peter Bonetti had just come in as Chelsea's goalkeeper and I admired him very much, especially as my old man used to take me there behind the goal and I could watch him from close up, throwing himself around like an acrobat, but I wanted to score goals, not to stop them. I think that's natural in a kid.

I must have been about twelve, I was a winger then, quite small for my age, and we were playing another school up on Wormwood Scrubs, in a knock-out competition. Very bleak it can be up there, and I remember that afternoon well, one of those days when you've got the east wind coming across the Scrubs and nothing to stop it. After about twenty minutes our goalkeeper went down for a ball and got kicked on the shoulder; he couldn't raise his arm any more and he had to come out. He was a good goalkeeper, I remember that, and I don't think he'd ever been hurt before. In any case we hadn't got any plans for when he *was* hurt.

There was a lot of argy-bargying, nobody much wanting to take over, till in the end, the master that was in charge said, 'Well, he'll have to play on the wing, so you might as well go in, Ronnie,' and I did.

I'd fooled around in goal in the playground, of course, mostly with tennis balls, plastic balls, and that, like everybody had, and I was a fair cricketer, as well, but I'd never reckoned to play there in a match before. I remember thinking how enormous the goal was, all that space and me so small. There wasn't even a net to make it seem, like, a bit cosier. The first shot that come in hit the bar. It's funny; I can still remember that, too, I can remember it sailing over my head, and thinking that it wasn't fair, how could I be expected to reach *that*, then the smack, and seeing the ball rebound over me again, with just as little chance of touching it as I had the first time. It's a terrible feeling, that kind of helplessness, like a nightmare. For the next few years, until I really started growing, I used to pray at nights that I'd grow, I used to stretch myself, everything.

My father, he was very good about that. I remember he'd come in and sit by the fire in his old postman's uniform in the mornings, after his first round, and he'd say, 'Well, there was Harry Hibbs, Ron, wasn't there?' Then we'd hear all about Harry Hibbs, what a great goalkeeper he was before the war, and only five foot nine. 'And what a positional sense!' the old man used to say. 'Positional sense; that's what you need, Ronnie. You need that, a goalkeeper, more than anything else in the world. With Hibbs, people always used to say they shot straight at him, but that was because of his positional sense. He was always, always in the right place.'

So I'd think to myself, maybe I'd be like Harry Hibbs, I'd be five foot nine with this great positional sense. The other thing my father used to say, which encouraged me, was, 'Don't forget there's low shots as well as high shots. The bigger the goalkeeper, the longer it takes him to get down.' The only trouble was that at that time, I couldn't imagine myself even growing to five foot nine. What I was, was about five foot one or two. If I could have been sure then of reaching five foot nine, I'd have been very happy. In fact if somebody had told me then I was going to grow to five foot ten and a half, I think I'd have gone mad, I'd have been so happy. I've heard they're working on things where doctors are going to be able to tell one day, this boy's going to be six foot, this one's going to be five foot three. I only wish they'd had them when I was a kid, though, mind you, it wouldn't be so good for the old five foot threes, would it? At least they might have a few years *thinking* they were going to be bigger than they were.

So there I was, out on the middle of the Scrubs, a horrible, cold, soggy day, the ground all squashy underfoot, and this ball sailing over my head and coming back again off the crossbar, just like I wasn't there. To make matters worse, I'd had to put on the goalkeeper's jersey that *he*'d been wearing, and it was miles too big. Even when I rolled up the sleeves it came drooping down, right over my shorts. I was cold and I felt terrible and I was thinking, why did they have to pick on me, it's ridiculous, picking on a little bloke like me.

Nothing happened for a while after that, I just stood and shivered and felt sorry for myself, till suddenly the other side came away and there was this forward coming through on his own and our centre-half, he was right out of it, shouting, 'Come on, Ron, come off your line, Ron!' The bloke must have reckoned it was odds on a goal, only this little fellow standing in his way, and I must say I'd have laid odds on it myself. I started off my line, like they were telling me, this player, he was a pretty big bloke, came thundering on, and suddenly, just as if it was natural, I dived, and there was no one more surprised than me when I realized I was hugging the ball. Everyone was yelling, 'Good old Ronnie, well played, Ron!' and I got up, all plastered with goo, and I kicked the ball away as far as I could – which as it happened, wasn't very far.

Still, I didn't let through a goal, I made another save or two and in the end we won the game. From that moment, I was a goalkeeper. Nobody really said do you want to or don't you, they just all naturally assumed it, and I suppose I went along with them. As for the bloke who'd been keeping goal, when he got better, they played him in my place, which is typical school football. But although I was playing in goal, in the matches, anyway, it was a bit of a time before I regarded myself as a goalkeeper. In my imagination, I was still Jimmy Greaves, the little bloke who ran round all the big ones and scored goals which, being a little bloke, was only logical, really. In the playground, I wouldn't go in goal at first because I didn't enjoy it, or rather I quite enjoyed it, provided it wasn't too cold and there weren't too many high shots, but I enjoyed scoring goals better.

I suppose the turning point came when they picked me for the district team. We only had one other player in it, my school, the centre forward, and when I heard I was picked, first of all I thought it was a joke and then, to tell the honest truth, I was in two minds about it. Because I think I realized then at the time, I'd been classified. I was a goalkeeper, whether I liked it or not, and if I was ever going to get anywhere as a player, and no one in the school ever thought about anything else, it would be in goal.

It was Hammersmith Schools we played, I think, and we did quite well against them; it was a draw or we lost by the odd goal, something like that. The only thing I really remember about it was I saved a penalty, which for a goalkeeper is about the nearest you can come in satisfaction to actually scoring. The penalty I remember very well. The bloke that took it was strictly right-footed, I'd already got the habit of watching players pretty closely, and anyway, he'd thumped in a few hard ones earlier on. To me, if he was right-footed, it probably meant he'd put the ball to my right, which was the natural swing. When he set himself for his run, I *knew* he was going to put it there, it was just impossible from that angle, the one he was coming at the

12

ball from, to put it anywhere else. As it happened it wasn't a very good kick, either, it couldn't have been much more than a yard from me, and I dived to it and held it. After that, they picked me for all the other games that season, too.

So I was a goalkeeper, and when I went to Stamford Bridge now, sometimes with my old man, sometimes with some of the other lads from our buildings, it was always, always behind the goal, to see what I could learn. Jimmy Greaves had gone, so it wasn't so difficult to start hero-worshipping Bonetti. He was called The Cat, and to me that fitted him perfectly. He could spring like a cat, fantastic heights, and throw himself about on the ground like he was made of indiarubber. A thing that encouraged me about him, too, was that he wasn't all that big. He was quite tall, though not exceptionally, but he was slight. Everything he did, he did because he was quick and because he was brave. I suppose if I modelled myself on anyone I modelled myself on him, which was good in a way, and bad.

The thing about Peter is, he's a very special sort of goalkeeper, at least in English conditions, heavy mud and that, and everybody going for the goalkeeper; he's a Continental type of goalkeeper, which you'd expect, because although he was born in England, his family comes from the Continent as you would guess from his name. The other thing is that whereas I *was* small and pretty thin, I'm not that now, I'm a pretty big sort of fellow, and in a way maybe some-one like Gordon Banks would have been a better model for me than Peter. Still, I don't regret it. I learned a lot watching him, and if some of the fans used to write him off for being flashy, I always reckoned that this was part of Peter; he *did* take risks, he did sometimes let himself down, but if he hadn't taken them, he wouldn't have made the saves he did, which were often beyond any other goalkeeper – balls that were as good as in.

The other thing was that having a goalkeeper like Peter Bonetti to admire made you feel better about *being* a goalkeeper.

You could see there was something in it, you didn't just have to be the old last line of defence, the bloke that always got blamed when he gave a goal away, who couldn't make a mistake without it being fatal. I even started going in goal in the playground, though being Peter Bonetti was a bit painful and all, on that hard surface. The high balls were all right, but now and again you'd forget yourself and dive for a low one. There were times when I'd come home covered with bruises. On the whole though, I think I got a lot out of it, this keeping goal in the playground; it toughened me up for later on. Because in English football you've got to be tough for a goalkeeper, it's a man's position. Sometimes when I've played abroad I've envied these Continental keepers, the way they're left alone and treated like little tin gods. It's easy to be a goalkeeper there, or anyway, a lot easier, which is another reason for admiring Peter Bonetti, because he can do the Continental stuff without any of the protection that the Continentals get.

After playing in the schools district side, I sort of went on from there. In fact it's a kind of escalator, and once you're on it, providing you have a bit of luck, it just takes you along. You may not go all the way, of course, not right up to schoolboy international and maybe, later on, youth international, but you'll go some of it. In my case, I got into the London schoolboys' side, then from there into the schoolboys' trials, which was the most exciting thing that had happened to me in my life. I'll never forget the day the sports master told me about that; but that was where it stopped.

Personally, I've never gone very much on trial games, because to me, they're artificial. You haven't got two teams that are playing against each other and making it a real game, you've got twenty-two individuals all playing for their place, all trying to look good, which isn't fair on anybody. It was South v. North that year. The North had a very good side, a lot of them went on to make full professional, several of them, three or four, even full international, and the South got hammered.

Sometimes that can be good, because, like I said, you get plenty of chance to show what you can do; and especially in a trial match, where the other goalkeeper may just stand around and do nothing. But it was seven–nil, and although I reckon not more than a couple of those were really my fault, I felt very dejected when I came off. I knew there wasn't much hope for me, and it didn't surprise me when the other fellow got picked.

Dad was very good about it, he'd been up there to see the game; it was in Derby, on the Derby County ground. He said, 'You didn't have a chance. That defence of yours was rubbish.' But that was that. The three games they had that season, I was substitute for two of them, and the other one they made someone else the substitute. I suppose they wanted to pass it round, like, though the old man said, 'That's ridiculous, that is. Dropped you from being substitute, I don't see how they could do that. What's the matter, didn't you sit up straight on the bench, or something? Didn't you stand up properly when they played the National Anthem?'

One of those three matches, the first one, against Wales, was at Wembley Stadium, and that was an incredible experience. Even to be substitute there was frightening, and I knew what people meant when they talked about Wembley nerves, all the goalkeepers who'd made terrible boobs there and cost their side the match. In fact, I was quite relieved in a way, sitting on the bench and watching, that I wasn't playing, although when you play, you tend to lose all that, you get absorbed in the game, while on the bench, you're part of it and you're not part of it; the atmosphere works on you.

And what an atmosphere! I'd never been to Wembley at all before, not even to watch a match, though I'd seen it often enough on television. And a schoolboy match is something different. The crowd's as big as you get for a real international, nearly as big as a Cup Final, ninety thousand, but they're all schoolboys, and the noise is unbelievable, very high-pitched, shrieking and whistling and booing. It's marvellous in a way, but in another way, for a kid not used to crowds at all, it can be shattering.

By this time, as you can imagine, there was only one thing in my mind. I was going to be a professional, and I was going to play for Chelsea, I'd take over in the end from Peter Bonetti. In fact I was going to be the second Peter Bonetti. I was all for writing in and asking Chelsea for a trial, but my father was against it. He knew quite a bit about the game, he'd been a fair amateur in his day, in fact I reckon he might have made something, if the war hadn't come along. He said, 'Don't write to them, Ronnie, let them come for you.'

I said, 'Yeah, that's fine, but what if they don't come? What then?'

He said, 'Of course they'll come, all the London clubs will come, especially the ones from round here. When they do, just tell them you're waiting for Chelsea.'

In fact the first one that come after me was Queen's Park Rangers, which was natural, really, because they were the nearest of all. At that time, though, they were only a Third Division club, and I didn't fancy them too much. I went up there and I played a trial, but when they wanted me to sign on schoolboy forms, I said I'd think about it. I suppose if it had been a few years later, when Rangers were in the First Division or doing pretty well in the Second, when they had Rodney Marsh there turning it on, I might have said yes, but though it *was* the local club, and some of the lads went down the Bush on Saturdays, most of us were for Chelsea.

We wanted to see the big stuff, the star names, and I suppose it was understandable, really.

Then, just after I'd got in the London schools side, it wasn't Chelsea that came after me, it was Borough. The first I knew about it was actually after a school match on the Scrubs. I'd noticed this white-haired old geezer standing behind the goal and watching. I'd stopped one or two and he'd said, 'Good save, good save.' Then, when the game was over, he sort of fell into step beside me, looking around like he was afraid he'd be seen, and he said, he was all nods and winks, 'Not signed for anybody, yet, have you, son?'

'No,' I said, 'I haven't.'

'How about Borough,' he said. 'Ever thought of them? Like to join them?'

'I don't know,' I said. I was cautious, first of all because I never *had* thought of Borough. To me, like, being a North London club, they might as well have been on the moon, they might as well have been Manchester United or even Celtic. The other thing was I couldn't be sure whether or not he was having me on, because now and again it happened to us. There was one old bloke come up to Tommy Withers when we were all kicking about on a playground up Notting Dale, not the school one, we must have been about twelve or thirteen, and he said, 'I have been watching you, son. Want a trial with Chelsea?' Well, to us, that was like saying, do you want a million pounds? Tommy didn't even think twice, none of us did, because the bloke looked okay, in fact funnily enough he seemed more like what you'd expect a football scout to be than the one from Borough. So Tommy said, 'Cor, fabulous,' he was a big boy for his age and one of the best footballers in the school.

The bloke said, 'Okay, be at Stamford Bridge tomorrow evening at six and bring your gear.' Tommy didn't talk about anything else until the time came, he walked about in a kind of daze, you could see in his mind he was already wearing that old blue jersey, he was captaining them at Wembley. Then of course he got along to the ground and nobody had heard of him. As for the old bloke, he never turned up again, which was just as well for his sake.

I think that did something to Tommy, because after that he was never really the same player; it seemed to knock some of the ambition out of him. He did quite well, although he never turned pro. The last I heard of him I think he was playing centre-half for Hendon, amateur. So naturally I was cautious.

Another thing, the bloke was still doing all this looking around, which made you wonder about him, though looking back, I reckon all it meant was he was worried about the master seeing him, illegal approaches to schoolboy players, and that.

Anyway, he knew my name, he kept calling me Ronnie, maybe he'd asked somebody. He wanted to know where he could get hold of me. I wasn't that keen at first, but then I gave him the address and he wrote it down, scrawled it on a bit of paper in the palm of his hand, like he was hiding it. Then he said, 'Here, here's my card,' it said JOE BENNING, Scout, Borough United F.C., and had his address. He said, 'You can phone me if you want to,' then he went off whistling. One or two of the other boys wanted to know who he was, but I just said, 'I don't know, I never seen him before,' remembering what happened to Tommy.

The funny thing was that I wasn't so much excited, I was sort of confused. He seemed to be genuine, and of course if he was it was a marvellous chance, but Borough wasn't Chelsea. In fact I couldn't remember how many times I'd stood there on the terraces calling Borough all the names under the sun, or going over to North London and cheering for Chelsea on *their* ground, with their supporters threatening us – you didn't get so much then of the actual terrace fighting that came later. Mind you, by this time I wasn't seeing too many Saturday games, because I was mostly playing in some representative or district match or other, I could only go when they were played in the mornings.

When I got home, they were all of them sitting in the kitchen, the old man, my mother, my sister, who's a couple of years younger than I am. The old man said, 'How'd you get on, then?' like he always did. I said, 'Won, 3–1,' and he asked me how I come to let one in, was it my fault and that; as usual. Then I told them, I said, 'A bloke came up to me and give me this card.'

The old man took it and looked at it and said, 'Borough, this is something, Ron.' He got very excited. I said, 'Yeah, I know, but it ain't Chelsea.'

'Well,' he said, 'but never mind, it's a First Division team, isn't it? It's a wonderful chance, Ron. I mean, supposing Chelsea never come to you? Or supposing you go there on trial and they turn you down?'

'They could turn me down at Borough and all,' I said.

'Yes,' he said, 'but they've come to you, haven't they? That's the difference. *They* want *you*. You haven't had to go to them.'

To me, I couldn't really see what difference that made, but the old man kept on at me, he said there was nothing to lose by going for a trial, and in the end I said all right, I would. Then I went out and looked for Mike.

You usually knew where to find him, especially at this time of year, with the evenings getting lighter. He'd be up on this playground we used for football. It was council property, just an open space with an asphalt surface and wire-netting all around it, with a couple of swings and a chute for kids in one corner.

Mike would turn up there with his bicycle; pushing it, you hardly ever saw him riding it. It was one of those big, black, heavy iron old things, nothing fancy about it, none of the old drop handlebars and plastic mudguards that some of the boys had. Mike was someone that we all looked up to. He had black hair, a lot of it with a lot of cream on it, always very neatly combed back in a square sort of style, a pale face – and bicycle clips. I don't think I'd ever seen him without the bicycle clips, whether he was playing football or he'd just got off the old bike. He lived for football, football was his religion, and he really knew the game. He'd been a bit of a player himself, a good amateur, I think, he'd drop the odd name now and then, Walthamstow Avenue and Leytonstone, and he said he'd once had a trial for the Wolves but turned down terms, because in those days there was a maximum wage, and it was very low.

There was a bit of a mystery about him. He lived somewhere about the neighbourhood, nobody quite knew where, and probably on his own. Now and again one of the lads said he'd seen him, somewhere round the back of the Harrow Road, apparently on his way home – cycling, of course – but at those times, Mike never said much, he'd just wave and go on his way. Nobody knew what job he did, either, that was something else he'd never talk about, but whatever it was, it seemed to give him plenty of time during the day. He'd join in quite a lot of our games in the playground; he was slow but a very neat ball player, very neat, you could see he must have been useful once; but if you ever came in on him with a hard tackle he'd say, 'Oh, me leg, me leg,' which was the one that was meant to have finished his career.

Quite often he'd come along and watch us play matches, too, over the Scrubs. He'd lean on his bicycle up near the goalpost and rabbit to me, I was doing this wrong, I was doing the other wrong; he was a great one for telling you what you were doing wrong, Mike. Then just now and again he'd give you a big smile and say something like, 'I was really proud of you, Saturday, Ronnie. I thought you'd really come on,' and that would make you feel tremendous, much more than if you got it from the old man who after all was your father, so he wanted you to do well.

When I first started keeping goal, Mike was a bit discouraging. 'Ronnie,' he'd say, 'your only hope is if you grow. You've got a lot of promise. A lot of ability. But those high crosses, Ronnie. Those are the things that matter. Those are what separate the men from the boys. You've got to have height to deal with those,' which didn't do much for my confidence. Still, he gave me a lot of useful tips on things like angles, when to come out and when to stay on my line. Now and again he'd be there when I'd let through a goal in a proper game and he'd tell me how I'd come out when I shouldn't, or I'd left too wide a gap, or whatever had happened. Or he'd be there behind the posts and yell out, 'Now!' when a forward was coming through on his own, and then I'd go, and it would often work. The only thing was, Mike was always right, there was never any other opinion, which may be why he liked to stick with boys, because boys don't give you so many arguments.

Anyway, there he was that evening, right enough, kicking around in the playground, showing the lads some fancy traps and flicks, and nodding the ball about a bit; he was good with his head. He called, 'Let's have you in goal, Ronnie,' and I went in what we called the goal, which was a space between two of the posts that held up the railings, more or less the proper width apart. There wasn't much chance to talk to him at first, because he was heading in crosses at me, backheeling volleys and all that, and giving me the odd bit of advice like he always did: 'Don't catch those, put 'em over, Ronnie,' and the rest of it. Then when a few more of the lads turned up and there was enough of us to pick up for a game, I was able to speak to him. I said, 'Borough want me for a trial, Mike.'

Well, that really stopped him in his tracks. He said, 'Borough? Want *you* for a trial? Straight up, Ronnie?'

I said, 'Yeah. Stand on me.'

He said, 'Who'd you hear from? Charlie Macintosh?' – which was the manager.

I said, 'No, this bloke here,' and I showed him the card; I'd brought it along with me. Mike looked at it, he turned it around and upside down, he ran his thumb across it, and at last he said, 'Joe Benning, Joe Benning, I've *heard* of him,' like if he'd heard of him, he must be the real thing. I said, 'A grey-haired old bloke. Very cheerful.'

'Yes,' he said, 'yes. He's not the *chief* scout, because the chief scout's Bobby Lawrence, he came after me when I was playing senior amateur. But he *could* be genuine, Ron, I reckon he *could* be genuine. I just don't want you to get disappointed, son, that's all. I mean, we know what happened to Tommy.'

'Yeah,' I said, 'I was remembering that when he talked to me, up the Scrubs.'

'But if it *is* true, Ronnie,' he said, 'then I'm very, very pleased for you. I'm delighted.' Then he smiled at me and said, 'Even if it isn't Chelsea.'

I said, 'Yes, I'd certainly rather it was Chelsea.'

He looked at me again and said, 'You're a funny bloke, Ronnie, aren't you? Not excited at all. If it had been me it happened to, I don't know, I'd have been doing handstands. I remember the first time *I* got asked for a trial. It was only Brentford, but I didn't sleep all night.'

I said, 'Yeah, but it isn't Chelsea, is it?'

'Well,' he said, 'you *are* odd,' and he looked me up and down. 'A League club comes along, a First Division club, and you start picking and choosing. What'd happen if everybody thought like you? If they only wanted to join the clubs they supported? Every Scottish kid would join Rangers or Celtic. Half the lads in England would go to Manchester United. And what about the Geordies? Every club in the country has three or four. What if they wouldn't sign for anyone but Sunderland or Newcastle United?'

'Well,' I said, 'I suppose you've got a point there.'

'Another thing,' he said, 'how about transfers? Players get bought and sold, Ronnie. They don't just stay with the same club for life, do they?'

'No,' I said, 'they don't.'

'All right, then,' he said. 'Suppose you do sign for Chelsea and they don't keep you. Have you ever thought of that? Or something else; maybe you'll join another club, Borough or someone, and later on, Chelsea will buy you. That's possible, as well. And you'd go straight into the first team then.'

He was very convincing, Mike was, and it ended up with his talking me round. By the time I got home I was really wanting it to be real, I was only afraid that maybe the old boy had been having me on. Every morning when the post came I was down there before anybody, or when I got back from school in the afternoon, the first thing I'd ask my mother was, 'Any letters for me?'

In the end it came. One Saturday morning, what a morning that was, a letter from Borough United saying would I attend a trial the Saturday after, be at their ground to catch the motor coach at half-past nine. I was in a schools county game that afternoon, but I reckoned I could fit both of them in, and that morning I was at the Borough ground an hour before the coach left. In fact I wasn't even the first, there were already three or four other kids sitting in the hallway there. The commissionaire on the door smiled and said, 'Bit early, aren't you?' like he thought it was funny, and these kids and I just sat there. We hardly said a word to each other, we were all too nervous.

Because it makes quite an impression on you, this big marble hall, very imposing, and you start thinking about all the famous players that have passed through it. In fact while we were waiting there one or two came in, there was Dick Rose, the big centre-half, who seemed a nice enough sort of fellow, joking with the commissionaire, and Sammy Frost, the winger. They give us sort of a half glance, then they went through the door marked PRIVATE; No ADMITTANCE, and I wondered would I ever be going through that door.

Gradually more boys started to arrive, all with their boots in bags or parcels, and we chatted a little. Most of them seemed to be from the London area, like me. Then we heard the coach pull up outside, and finally Reg James turned up, who was in charge of the youth team. He was a very tall man, in his forties, I suppose, and I rather liked the look of him, the way he smiled. He said, 'All right, lads, let's be having you then; is everybody here?' and checked us against a list he'd got. It turned out we were all there except one, and he arrived all puffing and panting, a little fellow with red hair, and Reg James said, 'Got to be quicker off the mark than that, son, if you're ever going to make a professional footballer.'

We were playing the trial over at Ruislip, where Borough had a training ground; I remember it being a very long ride. Reg was very nice to us, and so was one of the other youth coaches, Willy Pratt, both chatting and laughed a lot, but I didn't feel much like talking, and nor did the kid beside me, the little red-haired one. He kept saying, 'Missed me train, missed me train.' It was obviously worrying him. I told him, 'Never mind, you're here now, aren't you?' but it didn't seem to console him.

On and on we went, right out of London, right out into the country, which was nice, the fields and that. Living where we did in town we didn't see the country a lot, not unless we went on holiday to the sea, or maybe now and then when the old man took me to a match on an excursion train, and then only out of the train windows. I think I'd have appreciated it a lot more, though, if it hadn't been for knowing what was coming at the end of it, and wondering how I'd play.

I'd tried to make out who the other goalkeeper would be. It certainly wasn't the little red-haired bloke, he was much too small, and anyway when I asked him where did he play he said, 'Outside right,' like he was ashamed of it.

When we got there, the pitch was right out among the

24

fields. Not like the Scrubs, a huge open space surrounded by railway tracks and houses and that great big gloomy prison, but real fields, like a farm. They made us up into two teams, reds and blues – which were the Borough colours, blue and white stripes – and I was in the blues, which seemed like a good start.

The first minute, I gave away a goal. What a terrible start. It wasn't my fault, I don't think anybody could have stopped it, but it was a terrible feeling, that; to pick the ball out of the net, the first time I touched it. And that made it twice as bad because, like I said, I hated picking the ball out myself.

It was a deflection. The other side, the reds, came away from the kick-off, their left-winger went past our right-back, who was very, very slow, and crossed it. Their centre-forward swung a foot at it, about fifteen yards out, and I had it covered, no trouble, till one of our defenders stuck out his leg and it went off him into the opposite corner. I was caught completely off balance, there was nothing I could do. He said, 'Sorry, mate,' and I just shrugged my shoulders; all I hoped was that Reg James, who was reffing the game, had seen what had happened, and didn't blame me. If I'd only known then the trouble I was going to have with deflections, playing professional, maybe I'd never have turned. The times you're just waiting to collect a ball till some clown on your own side swings at it and puts it past you, then you read in the paper next morning that you're meant to have misjudged it. Sometimes the television puts that right, if they've filmed the match, and then it's you who have the laugh, because it shows quite clearly that you never had the chance, and the bloke that wrote all that rubbish is the one that looks silly.

But that was a long, long way ahead. In fact at that moment I wouldn't have given much chance on my turning professional for anyone, let alone for Borough.

The next bad thing was we turned out to have a much

stronger side than they had, despite the goal; I suppose they hadn't known all that much about the players, just put them in their right positions and hoped for the best. So there was me, left with nothing to think about except the goal I'd let through, and there was this kid down the other end, diving and leaping and punching all over the place, because our forwards were hammering them.

I thought he did quite well, though he had a lot of luck. He was very brave, he'd come out and dive at anything, sometimes head first, like a lunatic. A couple of times one of our forwards would be through on his own, and he'd come out and block it at his feet, But he was rash, he'd sometimes rush off his line when there was no need to, and to me, he tended to punch too much when he could have caught the ball. That was something Mike had always impressed on me, 'Catch 'em if you can, Ronnie; only punch 'em if you're under pressure.' I did get a couple of crosses to deal with, late in the half, and I thought I took them quite well, but that was about it.

At half-time I thought maybe he'd change the teams a bit, but he didn't, he just left them as they were, so, in the second half, it was the same old story. Plenty for him to do, nothing for me. Half-time was one-all, and in the second half we knocked in another two or three. Just in the last minutes, mostly through our team getting overconfident, they broke away, and two of them were clear, with only our centre-half to stop them. They interpassed, and got by him, but I'd read it quite well. I was off my line very quick, I dived on it with my shoulder into the bloke's legs, and I managed to roll over, holding it. It wasn't a lot, but I thought maybe it would be enough to get another chance.

In the bus, some were cheerful and some were quiet, most of the cheerful ones being our side, that had won. Reg James had said, 'All right, lads, you'll be hearing from us – some of you will,' which was enough to depress you. I didn't sit next to the little red-haired bloke, who'd played outside-right on their side, and hadn't done much, I sat next to our right-back, a quiet sort of boy from St Alban's with a lot of spots. 'Oh, well,' he said, 'I suppose that's that.'

'I don't know,' I said, 'you didn't do bad.'

'Nothing to do, was there?' he said. 'You were really unlucky with that goal of theirs.' You can imagine how much that cheered me up.

When I got home, they were all dying to know what had happened, how had I played, what was the score, but when they saw my face, they stopped smiling right away, I didn't have to tell them how it had gone. My mother, who was always optimistic for me, said, 'Never mind, you only let one in, they're bound to ask you again.' The old man said, 'Well, if they don't, they're not giving him a fair crack, and anyway, Ron, there's always Chelsea.'

'Yeah,' I said, 'there's always Chelsea.' To me, at that moment, it was like saying, there's always the moon.

I didn't even go round to the playground, I couldn't face it, Mike and all the questions. In fact I didn't go round for two or three days. I stopped rushing down for the post, too, though the old man was great about that, he even said he'd ask them to look out for a letter in the sorting office, if I wanted, but I said no, it didn't matter. In my own mind, I suppose I'd written it off, sort of to protect myself.

When I did go up to the playground, Mike asked, 'Well? How did you go?'

'All right,' I said, and he gave me one of those looks and said, 'You're disappointed, aren't you, Ronnie? What happened? Didn't they ask you back?'

'They didn't ask anyone back,' I said. 'They just told everybody they'd maybe let them know.'

'I don't like that,' he said. 'I'm not impressed by that. To me, with kids, you let them know one way or the other. You don't keep them hanging around in suspense.'

'Well,' I said, 'that's how they left it.' I must say I was very gloomy.

'But how did you *play*?' he said. 'You must know how you played, Ronnie. Did you have a bad one?'

'No,' I said, 'not really. I'd got no chance with the one that beat me, this early one, it was a deflection.'

'I hope you didn't get on and rollick your defence,' he said; he was smiling. 'Not like you sometimes do at the Scrubs.'

'No,' I said, 'I didn't say anything.'

Three days later, the letter came. Would I report to the Borough United ground next Tuesday evening, for training. I read the letter and the room went round. I just couldn't believe it. In fact I was in a daze all day; they asked me questions in class, and I didn't even hear them; they had to shout at me, one of the masters asked me was I ill or something. When I told the other boys, when I showed them the letter, they really flipped, they thought it was fabulous. Roger Gibbs, our left-half, who was one of the biggest Chelsea fans, said, 'See you let in a few down the Bridge, then, Ron.'

So next Tuesday, there I was, up at Borough. There were about twenty of us training, but I only recognized three or four of the ones who'd played in the trial match, and the other goalkeeper wasn't one of them. We trained in the big gymnasium they'd got, under Reg James, some sprinting and exercises and that, some of them with the ball, then some five-a-side games, then the other coach, Willy Pratt, took the goalkeepers; there were three of us. The other two were a tall lad with red hair from over Hackney, and a smaller one, blond, who come from Finchley. They were both a couple of years older than I was. We sort of eyed each other, like, 'How good's *he*?' Then Willy had us diving about on a couple of mats, a lot of this reflex stuff, him throwing short balls at you all the time so you had to keep changing your position, which was the sort of thing I liked. We didn't do any training out on the pitch, apparently they never used it, but just at the end Reg James came up to me and said, 'Want to have a look at the ground, then, son?'

I said, 'Yes,' and we went out there together. I remember we stood on the running track, red cinders. It was a very wet night, and the rain had left it all soggy. With the floodlights off, the terraces looked all ghostly, like cliffs in the dark. I looked at the two empty goals, and they looked very, very big.

Reg said, 'Want to walk on the pitch?' and we did. I stood in one of the goals, I was still pretty small. I jumped up and touched the crossbar, and Reg laughed and said, 'You'll have to grow!' Then he walked forward to a place just near the penalty spot and he said, 'This is where I got it. Blackburn. Went for the ball, centre-forward and I collided, broke my leg. Never played again after that; 1948, that was.'

I asked him had he been here all that time, and he said, 'Oh, yes, once with Borough, always with Borough. There isn't a club like it. Never will be. Who do you support, then? Anybody?'

I said, 'Chelsea,' and wondered had I been stupid. But he said, 'Well, Chelsea are all right, too, but you're at Borough now. If they take you on here, you won't want to change.'

I didn't think all that much about it at the time; after all there was a long, long way to go before I could even sign full pro for Borough, assuming they wanted me, but I've thought about it since. Because there definitely was this terrific spirit at Borough, Borough this and Borough that, this isn't Borough, that isn't Borough and yet, I don't quite know how to explain it, it all belonged to the past. Not just because it was to do with past players, people that you often hadn't heard of, but because I don't think people think the same way now, especially professional footballers. It's the same thing I find with my old man, when he talks about the Post Office, like it was something he ought to be grateful to, something that had always looked after him. Whereas to me, it was just a job. If it was steady it was because no one else wanted it, the hours were so long, there was so much walking and the pay was so low.

Time and again, I've heard the old man say, 'You kids now don't know how lucky you are. When I was your age I didn't have this, I didn't have that, if I wanted to see a football match I'd have to save up for three weeks.' Which was all of it probably true, only how were we expected to know? We could only know, like, what we'd been brought up to. It wasn't that we didn't appreciate things, I mean, to me my father and my mother were marvellous, we never went without anything, you could always go to them and talk about things, but this was *now*, and now was all we knew.

So for the next eighteen months or so I went on training up at Borough, and now and again fresh faces would appear, and now and again faces would drop out. One kid who became a particular mate of mine, Sammy Cunningham, centre-half, was really choked when they told him not to come back. He said, 'I don't know what I'll tell them, back at school. I don't know how I'm going to face them.'

I said, 'Well, never mind, maybe you'll get another club,' but he shook his head, really upset he was, because at that age, you haven't got a lot of confidence. He did turn pro, though. Later on he went to Luton and turned into quite a fair player.

Another one I liked was Danny Stroud, a centre-forward from out Slough way. He was tall for his age, and he had a lovely touch with the ball, beautiful control, he never seemed to hurry. Sometimes he looked like he was slow, but all it was, in fact, was that he took his time, he *made* time. You'd think, he's lost that ball, but then at the last fraction of a second his leg would stretch out and pull it away from the bloke trying to tackle him. He was good in the air, too, he got up very high indeed. When you played against him and a centre came across, you'd think it was your ball, easy, when suddenly he'd be up there with you, and maybe beating you to it, especially in that early time, when I was small.

Off the field he was the same, very casual, he didn't seem to care. Now and again he'd get a rollicking from one of the coaches for being too airy-fairy, for not trying, but it never seemed to worry him, he'd just smile and carry on with it, like to say, what's this silly so-and-so know about it, anyway? He had this confidence; I envied him. If there was one of us going to make it, you could see it was Danny.

So gradually, like I suppose you'd expect, I stopped thinking about Chelsea, I started thinking about Borough. It didn't happen all at once. I mean, I didn't take down all the Chelsea pennants and pictures that I'd got in my room and put up a lot of Borough ones. I didn't start going to Borough matches whenever I'd got a Saturday afternoon spare, though I did use to go in the week, which was partly because we could get in for nothing. It was just that I didn't think about Chelsea so much any more, about what Peter Bonetti and the rest of them were doing, I thought more about myself, what *I* could do. And if I was going to do it for Borough, well, it was natural I'd be interested in Borough.

One day when Roger Gibbs was round the flat and saying what a marvellous collection of Chelsea stuff I'd got, I suddenly said, 'You can have 'em, Rodge.'

'What,' he said, 'all of them? For nothing?'

I said, 'Yeah, go on, take them, all of them. All except Bonetti.'

So he did. He went round the room at a hundred miles an hour, like he was afraid I was going to change my mind, grabbing down all the photographs, the flags and all, till in the end there wasn't nothing left except Peter Bonetti;

31

though mind, I must have had about a dozen pictures of him, action shots and the rest. For me, Peter wasn't just Chelsea, he was what *I* wanted to be, an international goalkeeper, and I still reckoned I could learn from him.

Between fourteen and fifteen I must have grown nearly four inches, and that really encouraged me. Reg James told me, 'There you are; I told you you could do it if you put your mind to it, didn't I?'

As it got nearer and nearer my fifteenth birthday, I started to get worried. Were they going to offer me terms, apprentice professional, or weren't they? The old man wasn't as keen as I was, he said, 'Stay on a year, Ronnie, it's all education, isn't it? We can manage all right while you do.' But in my own mind, it was all worked out. I'd stay to the end of the school football season, the Easter term, when I'd be fifteen and a half, then I'd go apprentice pro with Borough. If they asked me.

Not but that a few others hadn't come after me in the meantime, Palace and Watford and even Spurs, till they found out I was already with Borough. When I got really worried, I'd tell myself that if Borough didn't want me, I could go to one of the others. But I knew that if Borough turned me down I'd be really shattered especially, like I said, as I'd never heard a dicky bird from Chelsea.

This was a thing between me and the old man, this business of me staying on at school. My mother, she didn't care so much about it, she'd say, if that's what he's set his heart on, let him do it. But to my father, it was amazing that I'd turn down what he'd always wanted. He said, 'Fourteen I was out of school, delivery boy. Up at half-past five every morning, and I *wanted* to stay on.'

'Well, Dad,' I'd say, 'they're different times, aren't they?'

'Yes,' he'd say, 'but education's education. You can break a leg, Ronnie, *then* where would you be?'

I thought to myself once, no worse off, I could always be a postman, but I didn't say it, I didn't want to hurt him.

Mike looked at it a different way from both of us. 'There's no hurry, Ron,' he said, 'not for a goalkeeper. A lot of goalkeepers don't even come into their own till they're thirty.'

'What do you want me to do, then?' I said. 'Stay at school until I'm thirty?'

'Just don't worry about it, that's all,' he said. 'They'll probably take you, anyway; you're definitely improving.'

The end of it was, they did take me. It must have been a week after my fifteenth birthday, and all that week I'd been killing myself, would they or wouldn't they? I started asking myself, did they know, which I knew was ridiculous because if there was one thing they always kept an eye on, it was that. Time and again I'd seen it, a kid that they wanted would be offered terms on his fifteenth birthday, though mind you there were a lot of others they weren't sure about that they didn't let go, but they wouldn't offer them apprentice pro, either. I was dead afraid that maybe I'd be one of those, neither one thing nor the other. On top of all that the weather was bad and I caught a terrible cold, my mother wanted me to stay home from school, but I reckoned if I did she wouldn't want me to go up for training, either; so I went.

That evening when I got to Borough the last thing I felt like was playing football. I was shivering a bit, I was sneezing all over the place, and Reg James looked at me, he said, 'You shouldn't have come tonight, son.'

'No, no,' I said, 'I'll be all right,' dead keen, and that, making the right impression. I can't help laughing now, when I think of the things you drop out with, a professional footballer, things not half as bad as that. Still, for all I knew that might have been the night they were deciding; they could always go and pick somebody else.

So I trained, and I played in the five-a-side game, and

afterwards I was sitting in the dressing-room, this smashing marble dressing-room they had, feeling a bit better after the bath, when Reg came in and said, 'The Boss wants to see you.'

Well, that moment, cold or no cold, I felt great, because I could see from the expression in his eye, sort of pleased for me, what it was going to be. I followed him up from the dressing-rooms, up the big old marble staircase, along the corridor, and then to the manager's office. He knocked on the door, a voice, a Scottish voice, called out to come in, so in we went. Reg said, 'Here he is, Boss,' and left me there.

The manager, that's Charlie Macintosh, was sitting behind his desk in a blue suit, which was unusual in itself, because you hardly ever saw him when he wasn't wearing a tracksuit. I'd met him quite a few times, but never for long; he'd come over occasionally and watch us training, but mostly he'd be gone by that time of night, and anyway, we were only kids. He was short but had big shoulders, very stocky, with wavy red hair, going back a bit. He'd been playing till about a couple of years back, right-back for Wolves, then player-manager with Rochdale, and then he'd come to Borough.

I remembered him very well at Wolves, because he wasn't too popular down the Bridge. He used to dish it out a lot and we'd have a right old go at him, 'Dirty Macintosh!' One day, I remember, he came up to the goal-line and gave us all a V-sign. I'd once seen him do a terrible foul on Frankie Blunstone; he'd got no chance at all of getting the ball and he hadn't even tried for it, just come across and kicked him about three feet up in the air. He was a Scottish international, though; but then we used to reckon, down the Bridge, that a lot of them were nutters. As manager, he'd done well for Borough. He had a reputation for giving youngsters a chance, which was one reason I'd been anxious to get taken on, because there were some clubs where obviously you had to wait for years.

He said, 'Want to turn professional, son?' and when he said that, well, I was walking on air, like. I said, 'You bet I do, Mr Macintosh,' and he said, 'Just call me Boss; Mr Macintosh is too formal. You can call me Mr Macintosh when I'm fifty – or when you're thirty,' which I liked. Then I thought of Mike and I started smiling. He asked, 'What's the joke?' and I said, 'It's just a bloke I know, sir, that says goalkeepers don't begin until they're thirty.'

'Well,' he said, 'you'd begin a bit earlier than that. We can't afford to keep you that long. What would your father think about your becoming an apprentice professional?'

I said, 'I think he'd agree,' and he said, 'Haven't you asked him?' I told him, 'Yes, he isn't against it, it's just he's got this thing about me staying on at school.'

'What about you?' he said. 'Do you want to stay at school, or do you want to come here?' and I got a bit frightened, I could see my chance slipping away, I was afraid he might say, well, if *you're* not sure you want to come, there's plenty that are. So I told him how I'd like to finish the season, see if I could get schoolboy international and that, and then I'd come. He said that was okay with him, and to bring my father along to see him. He said, 'What does your father do?'

I said, 'He's a postman.'

He said, 'Mine was a docker. Unemployed seven years. You're better off with football, son.'

I said, 'Yes, Mr Macintosh, I mean, yes, Boss, I know.'

By the time I got downstairs again the other lads were gone, but Reg was there, and he drove me down to the Tube. 'Well,' he said, 'coming to join us, then?'

'Yes,' I said, 'I hope so,' and he shook hands with me, he said, 'Put it there. You'll never regret coming to Borough, Ronnie. *I* never did.'

But like I said, Reg was a different generation.

A few days later, the old man came along with me to Borough to see Mr Macintosh. He wore his best suit, with a waistcoat, and he was very embarrassed, like he sometimes could be with people he didn't know, that he thought were important, swinging his hips about and looking away from them all the time.

The Boss was very friendly with him, very cheerful, laughing, making a lot of jokes. He said, 'I'm very, very relieved to meet you.' The old man said, 'And I'm glad to meet *you*.' I could see he didn't know *what* to say. The Boss said, 'I didn't say glad, I said, relieved,' and he looked from one to the other of us, my head to dad's head. He said, 'I was afraid you'd be a little fellow – like me!' The old man's about five nine. He said, 'I promise you this; if he grows as big as you, he'll play for England!'

Well, naturally that had the old man smiling, he moved about like he was tickled to death. He said, 'Think he's as good as that, do you?' and the Boss said, 'He *could* be as good as that. He's got the reflexes. He's got the courage. He's acquiring the judgement. What he needs is the experience. The sooner we can take him in hand full-time, the sooner we can start knocking the corners off him.'

The old man said, 'Yeah, well I appreciate that, don't think I don't, but there's his schooling; he's only just turned fifteen.'

'He can go to night school!' the Boss said. 'What do you want him to learn? Book-keeping? Engineering? He can go to a technical college if you want him to,' and I felt chuffed, looking at the old man, because this was obviously making him think again. He said, 'Yes, well, I suppose he could. Not that I'm not keen for him to play professional, not that I'm not proud you think so well of him, but what if he doesn't make it? You see what I mean?'

The Boss said, 'He'll make it. I can promise you that. The best young goalkeeper I've seen for years,' and I was walking on air, I can tell you.

The end of it was that Dad said yes, I could sign, as soon as the Easter term was over and the school football season, which he knew I wanted to play in. Charlie Macintosh said, 'Let's date it then and sign it now; then we can save a lot of other clubs bothering him,' which was fine with me, and the old man agreed with it, too. So the Boss brought in his secretary to witness the forms, and I signed. Apprentice professional. Five pound a week, working up to ten pound when I was eighteen. 'But by that time, we'll have him full pro,' the Boss said. 'Full pro at seventeen. No doubt about it; *no* doubt.'

So I signed and Dad signed and Charlie Macintosh signed and his secretary signed and there I was, apprentice professional with Borough.

After that I couldn't wait to start, especially after all the disappointment, not getting in the England schools side, and that. Going to school itself was terrible. I must admit I'd never enjoyed it very much, not the work side of it, the books. To me, it had been like marking time, and now it was worse than ever, knowing what was waiting for me when I left. The masters used to get at me about it, especially the one that took us for Maths, he'd say, 'Wake up, Blake, you're not playing for Borough yet,' or, 'You'd better pay more attention than that when you're keeping goal for Borough, Blake, or you'll let in dozens.'

Mike was really chuffed about it all. He said, 'I told you they would, Ronnie, I knew they'd take you. Now it's up to you, son. They'll sign you full pro, too, when you're seventeen. No doubt about that. None at all. And that's when the temptations start, Ronnie. That's when you've got to decide.'

I didn't quite get that. I said, 'Decide what, Mike?'

He said, 'Whether you're going to be a serious professional,' and I told him, 'Well, of course I am. That's all I want, isn't it?'

He said, 'Ah, that's what you want *now*, Ronnie. That's how you think *now* when you're living at home and you've not left school and life's a bowl of cherries. But there's a lot of temptations for a footballer. Things you don't even know about, yet. But you'll be all right as long as you remember one thing. Always put your career first. Always look after yourself; first and foremost. That one drink on a Friday night, Ron; that can cost a goal.'

Well, personally I'd never drunk more than the odd beer, but I said thanks very much, I saw what he meant, although I didn't, because what could be more tempting than football, at least for a fifteen-year-old kid like I was?

I didn't think I'd feel anything, leaving school, but funnily enough I did, it was a sort of empty feeling, at least for the first couple of days. I suppose it hadn't been too bad, really, I'd been fairly happy there, with the football and all, and everybody being interested in the game. They were very nice to me when I left, all wishing me luck, saying they'd be up to Borough whenever I was playing, and not to forget to keep coming over to the playground.

In fact I did keep going there, especially in the summer, when the professional season was over and I wasn't training with Borough any more. Then the season after that, it got a bit hectic, and I suppose I just naturally sort of drifted away. I know Mike got a bit upset about it at first. I met him in the street one afternoon, in the old Portobello Road, and he gave me one of his slow looks and said, 'Don't come over any more, then, Ronnie?'

'Well,' I said, 'not as much, I suppose. It's a bit difficult now, Mike,' and he nodded like it was what he'd been expecting.

He'd still pop up in places, though; you never knew where you were going to see him. You'd maybe be keeping goal in a youth game, or perhaps a South East Counties League match, and suddenly you'd hear from behind you, on the terracing, 'Hello, Ron,' or maybe, 'Stopped that one well, didn't you, Ronnie?' and there would be old Mike, though of course without the bicycle. Probably on his own, leaning over a crush barrier, because hardly anybody ever went to those games.

It was a nice life, apprentice professional, until you started getting near your seventeenth birthday, because then you got to worrying again; would they keep you? Although you *could* stay till you were eighteen hardly anybody ever did. At seventeen they made up their mind, and that was that.

Being an apprentice pro. was still quite new then. Before, they used to be called ground staff boys, helping around the stadium and that, sweeping up the terraces, giving the groundsman a hand with the pitch, studding the players' boots, and all, and I believe in some clubs, the smaller ones, this still went on. Not at Borough, though; their view was they were training you to play football, and the most you ever had to do was maybe lay out the kit for the first team on a Saturday morning. I quite enjoyed that, anyway, being in the dressing-room, thinking of who'd be putting on which strip, and of course imagining when *I* was going to be there and what it would be like, waiting for the buzzer to go, then trotting down the tunnel in front of maybe sixty thousand people.

Not that we were actually up at Borough very much; we used to train, all the juniors, out at Acton, and that was where we had most of our matches, too, on the little sports stadium. It was a fair old way to travel every morning, whereas most of the other apprentice pros were in digs round there.

Danny Stroud was another who used to travel in from home, though; from Slough. They'd signed him, like they had me, in fact I think they'd taken him on a week after myself. In a way we were a club without a club; we didn't really have a lot to do with the first team players. Some of them spoke to us, some of them couldn't be bothered. The goalkeeper then was Harry Vaughan, a Welsh international, a tall fellow with very big hands who used to chew gum all the time. He'd been around quite a long while, he must have been about thirty-two then, and he'd played a lot of games for Wales.

He was very strong, a lot heavier than Peter Bonetti, but very agile with it, too. Whenever I had the chance to watch him, I did. He was what I'd call the old-fashioned type of goalkeeper, very efficient, very sound, good on the line, strong on the crosses, good positioning, didn't often do anything fantastic, but hardly ever made a mistake, either. I'd certainly have settled for turning out as good as he was, but I think that secretly I wanted a bit more, I wanted to be spectacular, which you could understand in a kid.

He never said a lot to me and I was a bit scared to talk to him, like I was to most of the big fellows. One day, though, after a youth match up at the Stadium, he came up and said to me, 'Lift your knees up when you go for the crosses, son.' Just that. I said, 'Thanks very much, Mr Vaughan.'

He said, 'Harry'll do.' Then he said, 'Think twice about going up with you, then, forwards will. A goalkeeper's got to protect himself. The higher you go, the harder it gets.'

At first I thought he must be talking about the higher the ball was, but later on I realized he must have meant the League, and he was right. The more you saw, the better level you played, the more you were amazed at the kind of thing they'd try and pull on you.

Like the first time I played in Borough's reserve team, in the combination; I was still only sixteen. I came out to a corner, but just as I was shaping to jump for it a voice shouted, 'Leave it, Ronnie!' and of course I stopped, reckoning it must be one of our defenders. The next thing I knew, their centre-forward had headed it against the crossbar. The referee didn't notice anything; I'd have felt a right Charlie if it had been a goal.

Another time, when I said to Harry Vaughan, 'I wish I could hold a ball like you do,' which I did, he said, 'Chewing gum. Always put some on my hands. Rub it well in.' I thought he must be having me on, but later on I tried it and it seemed to work. Maybe it's just psychological, I don't know, but I still use it now and again, on a dry day when I don't need my gloves.

Another thing Harry Vaughan had was his cap. It was a terrible thing, a real old-fashioned cloth cap, not the kind that goalkeepers have these days, round and coloured with a long peak. It was so torn that you wondered how it hung together, in fact he hardly ever actually wore it, just took it out there with him and flung it into the net, always the first thing he did. He said once, 'First cap I ever bought when I went to work on a building site. Had it ever since.' Like I said, you find a lot of that sort of thing in football.

Sometimes I couldn't believe how lucky I was, knowing the kind of jobs most of the boys that had left with me had gone into, working as messengers or in shops or apprenticed in some factory. What I had was what they all wanted, and the only fear was that maybe I wouldn't keep it. Not that I hadn't got confidence in myself, but you saw so many who got taken on and then didn't get retained.

Like I remember one morning arriving at Acton for training and one of the lads, a winger called Gerry Forbes, from Glasgow, was sitting on his own in a corner of the dressing-room with his head in his hands, as though he'd been crying. I asked someone what was the matter and they said, 'They're sending him home.' And it was very quiet in that changing-room as if someone had died, and like the next time it might be one of us. I think we were all pretty shattered by it; not just sorry for Gerry, though we were – he was a good little player but a bit fragile, which may have been what decided them – but thinking, who's going to be next?

The only one who seemed to take it in his stride was Danny Stroud, I don't think it ever came into his head that he wouldn't make it; I must say I envied him.

'Plenty of other clubs, Gerry,' he said, like it was a joke. 'You can play for Rangers, now,' which of course didn't cheer Gerry up, because at times like that you don't feel you're ever going to play for anybody. Danny said to me when we were out training, 'I could have had Spurs, I could have had Charlton, I could have had Southampton.' I thought, yes, when you were a schoolboy, but what about when you're seventeen, like Gerry? I didn't say anything, though.

I was sixteen when I went abroad for the first time; with the youth team, to Nice, in the South of France, to an international tournament. I'd never flown before, either, which was another experience. In fact I don't think more than three or four of us had ever flown.

There we all were at London airport, in our blazers, all very smart, with Reg James looking after us, a bit like a schoolmaster, looking at one another, wondering what it was going to be like. Even Danny was a bit quieter than usual. We got in the jet, and when you take off, of course, there's that first moment, that tremendous rush of air when it gathers speed, and naturally you're not prepared for it, I certainly wasn't. You feel you've completely lost control of everything, you're just being swung up into space and anything can happen, you can crash, or maybe you'll just go up and you'll come down, because there's so much movement, so much power, carrying you away.

The lad sitting beside me, a full-back called Nobby Green, from Birmingham, was sick into his paper bag, and that didn't help me. I turned away and tried to think of something else, but what could you think of? Normally to distract myself I had this thing about catching high crosses, I'd be, you know, weightless, like in a waking dream, these balls, one after another of them, floating across in slow motion, and me floating up to catch them, ball after ball after ball. But it didn't work this time; how could you think of floating when you were going through space at the speed we were?

I closed my eyes, and when I opened them again, I don't know how long later, we were up, going very smooth now, no problems. I looked across Nobby, out of the window, down at the ground, and immediately I felt bad again, because it was all spread out like a map, everything green and very clear but God knows how far below, so that all you could think of was falling. Because once you're up in the clouds, like I found later, once you can't see anything but the sky, you're all right, you've gone into a kind of dream, haven't you? Nothing's real. But seeing things you know, seeing things so far below you, that's terrible.

Once we were up in the clouds I felt better, and the air hostess came round to Nobby, a nice girl, very pretty, and after a time he felt better, too. He was a good bloke, a proper Brummy, with that funny old accent of theirs. In fact we had all types in the apprentice pros and the juniors, quite a few from Scotland, three or four Geordies, from the North-East, a couple from Lancashire, but very few Londoners, apart from myself. I think Charlie Macintosh had this thing about boys from Scotland and the North, which I didn't agree with, naturally. He thought they were tougher, and they had more determination, whereas Londoners were inclined to give up when things weren't going right. He'd say, 'It's too easy for a London boy. Give me a boy from tough conditions,' which to me didn't make sense, because you couldn't come from much tougher conditions than I'd seen round West London. Still, he was the manager, and there was no arguing with him; I just had to prove that he was wrong by my playing, and Danny felt the same as I did. We used to joke about a bit with the boys from the provinces, how north of Barnet was the end of civilization, how people started talking a foreign language, and that.

Danny used to say, 'What's that, son? Don't understand you. Say it in English, will you?' In fact they *were* a bit hard for us to understand at first, some of them, just as I suppose we were for them, but it didn't really mean anything. After a time you all mucked in, it didn't matter where you came from; you were all professionals, all Borough players. And the funny thing was that though, like I've said, we were a different generation from Reg James and those, the pre-war professionals, and the ones who played just after, some of this Borough feeling did begin to sink in.

Mind you, they didn't half din it into us. You're playing for Borough. We don't do this at Borough. We won't have that at Borough. Now and then, Danny used to take the mickey; though not when anyone like Reg was listening. One of the lads might commit a foul, or maybe use bad language, something like that, and Danny would put on this high-pitched voice, 'Not at Borough, *please*! We don't do that at Borough!'

When my mother and father knew I was going to France, they got a little worried. The old man had been there in the war, with the army. He said, all embarrassed, like he always got when he had to talk to me about anything like this, 'Look after yourself there, Ronnie. You want to watch them French girls a bit.'

'Watch them?' I said, making out I didn't follow him. 'How do you mean watch them, Dad?' and he got more tied up still. He said, 'Just be careful, son, that's all. Just look after yourself.'

But what with the way they kept an eye on us there, Reg James and the others, there wasn't much chance of anything happening, even if we'd wanted it to. They looked very nice though, the French girls, when you saw them; they had this way of walking that was a lot different to what you saw at home, like they were very sure of themselves. It was a lovely place, too, Nice, with these wide streets along the seafront, the sunshine and the sea itself, though it was still March, and there wasn't any bathing. As for our hotel, I'd never stayed anywhere like it. The bedroom I shared with Danny was enormous, it seemed to go on forever, three times as big as the one I had at home. At first I admit I felt a bit homesick, only sixteen, first time I'd really been away, but Danny didn't seem to mind. He kept ringing for things, chatting up the maids, trying to make himself understood, and that. I remember him flinging himself on his back, on to the bed, and saying, 'This is all right, isn't it? Do me, this. I reckon I'll go on playing football.'

I felt like he did. If football could give you all this, what a life! Go everywhere, see everything, and all for nothing; just doing what you'd always most wanted to do, what millions of kids wanted to do. And this in a way made me all the more frightened over would I make it or wouldn't I; knowing there was so much to lose.

Reg James made us laugh a lot, there. He was a real Cockney, didn't speak a word of any other language even though I believe he'd been all over the place in the army during the war. Actually he did speak a few words, but I don't think even he knew which was what by now; things like *imshi* and *yallah* that he'd got in the Middle East, and *savvy*? that was another big favourite. He'd use all these on waiters and people, and of course they'd look at him like he was bonkers. He usually got what he wanted in the end, though, Reg. To me, he was great. I don't think I ever saw him lose his temper. Ever.

Playing against Continentals for the first time was a funny experience. It was a different game. There were a Spanish team, a French team, another from Italy, one from Germany, and some others. From my own point of view, I didn't mind it, because the first thing I noticed was the way they left the goalkeeper alone. In England, when you go for a ball, unless you've got about five yards to spare, there's always someone in on you, harrying you, hoping you'll make a mistake, or maybe trying to obstruct you and upset you. But not there. The goalkeeper's king out there.

I noticed it especially in the first game we played, against this Italian team. The way their keeper strutted about his own penalty area, you'd have thought he owned it, honestly. He wasn't a bad goalkeeper either, he was very acrobatic, but my goodness, the way he made things look hard when they could have been easy. Balls that I'd have strolled across to and practically picked up, he'd be positioning himself not so he could take them easy, but so that he *had* to dive for them. And the crowd loved it, that was the other thing that amazed me, because you would have thought they'd have seen through it; to me, it was all so obvious. But no; they'd cheer him like anything when he made one of his flashy saves. In fact it got to a point when Danny started applauding him too, when he'd made some easy save, just to take the mickey.

They were clever players, though, most of these Continentals. They didn't like to mix it, but they could do things with the ball that most of our players would never think of; kill it from all sorts of angles, play it off first time, on the volley. And the bicycle kick; this was another thing. Reg James had warned me about it; he'd said, 'Look out for bicycle kicks, Ronnie.' I asked him what he meant and he said, 'Overhead volleys, with their back to the goal. They take off on one foot and hit it with the other.' Which is a bit hard to imagine until you've actually seen it. In fact when it happened the first time, in this game against the Italians, it took me completely by surprise.

There was a ball coming across our goal at I suppose about three or four feet high, the kind you'd have to dive to head, and you'd be pushed to volley. Their centre-forward had his back to the goal, and there didn't seem to be any danger, when suddenly bang! he took off like a jet plane, one leg after the other, and with the second leg, he caught the ball a hell of a crack. I never even saw it; it had gone over my head, hit the crossbar and was back in play before I realized what was happening.

Reg said to me afterwards, 'There you are, Ronnie; I warned you,' I said, 'Yes, you did, Reg,' which was true. The difference was that now I'd know what to look for.

But they had a lot of tricks, the Continentals. They could bend balls – sometimes from free kicks, like the Brazilians do – they could make them dip, they could put backspin on them so you suddenly found them going away. Maybe they didn't always hit them as hard as English players did, but they could give you a lot of trouble. We didn't win a match in that tournament; drew two and lost the other to a Spanish team, that eventually won it. The only goal was one that taught me a lesson.

Their right-winger got the ball, beat our full-back, went to the line, and looked like he was going to pull the ball back across the goal, which is the natural ball in a situation like that, and very, very hard to deal with. I went to meet him and moved maybe a yard off the post – and as soon as he saw that, he hit it with the outside of his right foot, just between the post and myself. I felt a right clown, I can tell you.

Reg was very nice about it, like he always was when this kind of thing happened. He said, 'It's experience, Ronnie; that's what we bring you out here for. And give the boy his due, he took it well; he took it *very* well. I've seen plenty of experienced keepers beaten like that.'

'I looked a mug,' I said. Reg said, 'If you'd stayed on the post, he'd have crossed it. There's times a goalkeeper's got to gamble in this game, Ronnie. Anyway, a lot of players couldn't have squeezed it in from that angle; so it was probably the safer choice. Anyway, he shouldn't have been let through on his own.'

Which was very fair of him, seeing he was never a goalkeeper, but always a defender. Because you always have this thing going between goalkeepers and defences, whose fault was it? The defenders say, you didn't come off your line quick enough, it was your ball, and the goalkeeper says no it wasn't, it was too far out, it was a defender's ball. Or if a forward's through alone and scores, the defender who let him through might say to the goalkeeper, I thought you'd be off your line, that's why I didn't go with him, and the goalkeeper will tell him, don't be ridiculous, I'd got *no* chance, you dropped me right in it.

But I enjoyed the trip all right, even if we didn't win anything; it was amazing to think that people could live all the year round in places as beautiful as this, with the mountains and the sea and all. They were very hospitable, too; there were receptions and tours and we brought back some smashing presents. I got a silk tie for the old man and some perfume for my sister and a scarf for my mother. The flight back was a different story; I wasn't worried by it now, and it was fabulous, looking down on the mountains.

The nearer it got to my seventeenth birthday, the more worried I got; was it all going to slip out of my hands. It was like they'd run through a trailer for me of how it would all be. A trip or two abroad, like this one to Nice. Then games in the Youth Cup, taking you to places like Manchester United and Burnley and Wolves, only with hardly anybody there, so it was real and yet it wasn't real. Still, I thought, I'd *played* at these places, they couldn't take that away from me; and under floodlights, and all, which was another new thing for a goalkeeper, they'd worried me, the first time I'd played under them at Acton, though at Acton it was all shadows, at Manchester it was like broad daylight.

The old man did his best to cheer me up. 'Don't worry, Ron,' he'd say. 'The way you've been playing, I reckon they'll be afraid that *you* won't sign for *them*, that someone else will be after you.' But of course the old man saw it all from my point of view, he was as caught up in it as I was.

Mike spoke to me one day in Ladbroke Grove, when I ran into him. He said, 'Nearly seventeen now, aren't you,

Ronnie?' He always seemed to remember these sort of things. I said, 'Yeah, that's right,' and he said, 'Well, now you'll be signing full pro.'

'I hope so,' I said, though I must admit it encouraged me, hearing Mike say that, because normally he didn't give anything away, old Mike. He said, 'Why, you're not afraid they're going to give you the push, are you?'

'You never know,' I said.

'Always very cautious you are, Ron,' he said, 'that's what I like about you. Always modest. Good. I think it's a foregone conclusion. I saw you in the Youth Cup, over at Palace. Very nice, Ronnie. A very nice game. One mistake. That cross ball in the second half. The one from the left-wing.'

'Oh, yes,' I said, 'I remember. The centre-half called me off it, Mike.'

'Never blame your defenders, Ron,' he said. 'Never do that. How many times have I told you that? If you think it's your ball – shout for it. If they get in the way, knock 'em out of it. You've got to be assertive, Ronnie. There's nothing worse than a goalkeeper that doesn't assert himself.'

'Yes, Mike,' I said, 'thanks, Mike,' and I went away with the usual feeling I had when I talked to him, like I was still about twelve years old. But he'd definitely encouraged me.

And of course he was right. They did take me; right away. In fact I knew about it the day before I had my seventeenth birthday; down at Acton. Reg James came into the dressing-room with his big smile and said, 'Many happy returns of tomorrow, Ronnie. You needn't come in for training; the Boss wants to see you up at Borough. Bring your father. You can guess what he wants.'

I certainly could. The room went round for a minute, I didn't know what was happening, then Reg James was shaking hands with me and saying, 'Congratulations, Ron,' and several of the other lads came up as well.

Next day the old man and I went up to Borough; I practically floated up those stairs to the Boss's office. I signed the forms; it was a four-year contract with a four-year option, taking me up till I was twenty-one, starting at twenty quid, the money going up and up according to whether I played in the Reserves, or if I ever played in the first team. The words sort of dissolved in front of me, and the old man kept staring and staring at them, too, because some of the money, that I'd get if I was in the first team, with all the bonuses, was more than he'd dreamed of in his life.

Charlie Macintosh patted him on the back and said. 'By the time it comes to sign a new one, he'll have played for England,' then he got out a bottle of sherry and we all of us had a drink. To me, then, he was the best manager in the world.

Chapter 2

Two months later, I was playing in the first team. It was all so quick, I hardly knew what was happening. It seemed like one moment I was down at Acton, playing morning games in front of a few dozen people, the next I was coming out of that old tunnel at Borough on a Saturday afternoon into this great, big wave of noise, so loud that for a moment you were afraid it would wash you straight back down the tunnel again.

The first stage I was told that I wouldn't train at Acton any more, which was less than a couple of weeks after I'd signed full pro. I was very pleased, of course, very, very chuffed, but in a way I was uneasy, too; it was a bit like leaving home. All the blokes you'd grown up with since you'd been at Borough; Danny and those. Then Reg James who'd always been a right nice fellow, looking after you, encouraging you, making you feel at home. Maybe he was a bit easy-going, like some people said. Maybe he was a bit old-fashioned. Certainly he hadn't got any of that Football Association coaches' stuff that I met such a lot of later on, all the old codswallop about blind side running and zonal covering and positive running and the rest. But he'd got one thing, old Reg; he made you believe in yourself, he made you believe he was on your side, and I'd swop a lot for that. All the fancy language, for a start.

The day after I'd signed, I went up the playground to tell them; I was just going to throw it away, like, 'Oh, by the way, I've signed,' but Mike knew, he always seemed to know everything. 'Well done,' he said, as soon as he saw me – he was juggling around with a ball, as usual. 'Told you, didn't I?'

I was right surprised, I said, 'How'd you know, Mike? Who told you?' but all he said was, 'I know, I know,' in this way he had, like he knew everyone and everyone knew him, though coming to think of it now, I suppose maybe it had been in an evening paper or something. He didn't miss much, old Mike. He asked me what sort of a contract I'd got and I told him and he nodded like he thought that was okay. But he said, 'Should have had a word with me, though, Ronnie; I might have been able to help you. I mean, your old man, it isn't really his pigeon, is it?'

I said no, I supposed it wasn't – which it wasn't – though to be honest I was still walking on air, then. To me, it seemed a wonderful contract, any contract would have done. In fact I believe that if they'd offered me five quid a week, I'd have taken it; I'd have practically paid *them*!

On the other hand I felt a bit guilty, too, coming up and telling all the lads, a lot of them younger than I was, now. For this young lot, it wasn't so bad, because they could still dream of doing what I'd done. But for some of the older ones that still went along to the playground, blokes that had been at school with me, you could see in their faces what they were feeling. I think they were glad for me all right, but at the same time you could tell they were thinking, why's it him, why isn't it me? I went down the playground even less after that.

The senior players didn't train on the actual Borough ground, either; they trained out in Essex, at Snaresbrook, which was a lot farther from home than Acton. Most of them had cars, but I hadn't, and I couldn't even get a lift, what with the majority of players living near the club, in North London. I thought of getting a motor bicycle, I couldn't afford a car, but when Charlie Macintosh heard that, he nearly did his nut. He said, 'I'll not have any of *my* players risking themselves on those damn things!'

So it meant trailing over to Borough every day with the

three or four other lads who hadn't got cars, and getting a lift from someone, usually Billy Wallis, the coach.

He was a funny little fellow, Billy; very, very tiny, but he'd been a good player with Borough, I'd seen him once or twice down the Bridge, just near the end of his career. He was a London boy, like me, but from over Stepney. Very quiet, very shy, never said a lot, but when it did come out, it was sort of unexpected and sometimes very funny. Like once when we were playing a practice match out at Snaresbrook and it was diabolically wet, I dived at someone's feet on the ball, right into a puddle and Billy, who was reffing, looked down at me and said, 'Don't worry, Ron. I'll get you a snorkel.' Or another time, when I kicked out a very high ball, he looked up after it with this funny expression he had, sort of questioning, and he said, 'Gone into orbit, that one has, Ron.'

Now and again he played in the games himself, like Charlie Macintosh, and you couldn't have had two more different players. His control was lovely, Billy's, he could do anything with a football, juggle it from foot to foot until you got tired of watching him, flick it over his shoulder with his heel, pull it back with the sole of his boot then go on again, in the same movement; he was lovely to watch. 'Two stone more,' the Boss used to say, 'two inches more, and Billy would have been the greatest.' One day Billy looked at him, deadpan, and said, 'No, I wouldn't. I'd have been a player like you.'

In fact I don't think Billy could ever have been a player like the Boss, because their whole outlook was so different. Billy was obviously one of those quiet, thoughtful players, doing everything to inches, whereas Charlie Macintosh, even in the practice games, was just like I remembered him when we booed him at the Bridge, he still went in for every ball like his life depended on it, like a madman. He hated losing; even in some little potty five-a-side game.

I've seen him going in for really dangerous tackles on a

Friday morning, when there wouldn't have been time to get a player fit again, Billy warning him, 'It ain't a real game, Charlie,' and him saying, 'Every game's a real game,' which to him it was.

The thing about him was he'd been brought in from outside, it was the first time for I don't know how long that Borough had appointed anyone who hadn't played for them, and they'd done it deliberately, because they'd been slipping a bit from what they were, and a lot of people had criticized them for this; for being too narrow. So they'd fetched Charlie Macintosh in as sort of a new broom, and about the time I signed full pro he was starting to shake the team up a lot, bring in a lot of young players. So there were two camps, really, the young players who thought he was great, because in the old days you had to wait so long at Borough for your chance, and the older ones who naturally weren't so keen on it.

Billy was more or less in between the two. He'd been a Borough player himself, so naturally he was friendly with the older ones, but at the same time he'd been a youth coach before he'd been the senior coach, and the young players got on with him, too. You always felt you could talk to Billy, you never felt he was, like, in authority, whereas with the Boss, it was difficult to know how to take him. Sometimes he could be very friendly, others he'd start ordering you about, why hadn't you done this, why were you doing that. I suppose they were a good combination, really. While it lasted.

The first team goalie, Harry Vaughan, seemed to be a bit on the other side. Nothing much was actually said, at least while I was there, but there seemed to be these undertones. Looks they'd give one another now and then. Like in a practice match I was playing in and the Boss was refereeing, he shouted at Harry, 'Come on, Harry, that's your ball,' and Harry came out of goal, picked it off the forward's feet without bothering to dive, turned round and gave the Boss

54

this look, as if to say, don't tell *me* my business, then kicked it deliberately into touch.

The Boss made a joke of it, then, he said, 'What's the matter, Harry? Playing for time?' but he didn't look too pleased.

Not long after I'd begun training at Snaresbrook, Harry got hurt playing up at Newcastle, badly bruised ribs. Terry Morgan, the reserve team goalkeeper, moved up into the first team, and I got my chance in the Reserves.

Funnily enough we were away to Queens Park Rangers, the nearest ground to home, which was nice in a way, with all the family coming, all my friends, but in another, not so good, because it was an extra worry. Make a fool of yourself, and you did it in front of all of them.

In fact this was something I'd come more and more to think about as I started playing in the senior teams; would I have been better off with a club right outside London? Not that I wanted to leave London *as* London, of course I didn't, it was all I knew. For me, the provinces were like the moon. Worse, in a way, because on the moon at least you'd all be starting from scratch, whereas in the provinces, you'd be the stranger. On the other hand, especially for a goalkeeper, this was an advantage, because whatever you did, you did, so to speak, in foreign territory. You didn't have to run into people you knew in the street the day after you'd given away a jammy goal and have them saying, 'Hard luck,' or, 'How did you let that one in, then?' one being as bad as the other.

Not to mention Mike, who seemed to be everywhere, and who quite honestly used to get on my wick now and again, with his advice and all. I mean, I was grateful and that for what he'd told me, how he'd encouraged me, but I was a professional now and I knew what I was doing. When I did something wrong I knew that, too; I didn't need anyone to tell me.

So I started getting jumpy about this game at the Bush, I

began wishing it had been almost anywhere else; at Borough Stadium, or better still down at Portsmouth, Coventry, Leicester, somewhere like that, that was too far for Mike to cycle. Because I'd got this picture in my mind, me standing in the goal there, and behind the goal Mike and about a dozen others of the lads, leaning over the wall, calling out advice, telling me what I ought to do and ought not to do, and up in the stand, where I could see them, because there'd be hardly anybody else there, the old man, Mum and my sister. I could imagine the old man saying to the people round him, if there were any, 'That's my son, that is,' at the very moment I'd maybe misjudge the ball and let it drop in over my head, and they'd say, 'Oh, yes,' sort of sarcastic, 'done well with that one, then, didn't he?' In fact, I was having ridiculous thoughts like going in to see the Boss and asking for a transfer, him saying, 'Where to?' and me saying, 'Anywhere outside London. Manchester, Liverpool, Birmingham, anywhere; I can't stand it any more.' All ridiculous, but that's how it gets, when you're a goalkeeper.

Which was the point I was trying to make, before. It's different with an outfield player, even if he's, say, a centre-half or a full-back, who can give away a goal with a mistake. A goalkeeper's mistake nearly *always* gives away a goal. He's the one who's always got to carry the can. Anyway, you can understand how I felt before the game.

The crowd was very small, like I'd expected, there couldn't have been more than a few hundred there. The ground was terrible, like it often is down there in midwinter, hardly any grass, great puddles lying all over the place, and although they'd put sawdust in the goalmouth, you knew it was all going to churn up and you wouldn't have a decent take off. That's something else people often don't know about when they criticize goalkeepers; you start off going for a high cross – and you slip.

We had a fair old side out that day; three internationals,

five or six that had played in the first team that season. It was all part of Charlie Macintosh's policy to bring young players into the League side, which of course meant dropping the older ones. Naturally the ones that had been dropped weren't too happy about it, so the atmosphere wasn't all that good. Reserve football's fine if it's a step up, like it was for me, but for experienced players, people who may have played for their country, there's nothing much in it; which is why you get some funny results.

The centre-half was a bloke called Peter Morton, he'd played for Ireland, big and strong, very physical, one of those players that's on their backside half the game making sliding tackles, that I never like being behind, because they're always liable to sell themselves. Another thing about him that I'd noticed in practice games was that though he was good in the air, he got up well, he was inclined to back-pedal and crowd his goalkeeper. In a third team match or a youth game, where you feel confident in yourself, it wouldn't be so bad, but playing your first Reserve match, behind someone that much more experienced, you're nervous about shouting at them.

Mind you, he was very nice to me; he was always very cheerful. He smiled at me in the dressing-room and said, 'Don't worry, Ronnie, I'll keep them away from you!' Then what does he do in the first five minutes but put one past me himself?

It had all started off quite nicely, too. Running out, I heard a bit of a cheer and, 'Good old Ronnie!' which was nice, even if I hoped they weren't all going to be behind my goal, like I'd feared. In fact we went to the one on the right, and the shouts seemed to be coming from the other end. The lads sent in a few shots, and I thought I was holding them well. I'd put my gloves on immediately, and though the ball got wet right away, being a white ball, a plastic one, I knew it wouldn't pick up much mud.

Soon after we kicked off Bert Coe, the left-back, a

Manchester fellow, who'd played a long time in the first team, pushed the ball back to me so I could get a feel of it, an early one, which is something I always like. I picked it up, held it a few seconds, then he ran out to the wing calling for it and I threw it out to him, to begin what turned into a nice move. I felt encouraged. A few minutes later, I felt terrible. One of their side belted a long ball down the middle, and Peter Morton came after it with their centre-forward. There was nothing in it, really, no danger; I could even have come out to the edge of my area and kicked it away, if I'd wanted to, it was as easy as that. Or rather, it should have been. Normally I'd have called for it, and that was probably where everything went wrong; in the youth team I'd have yelled, 'Keeper's ball!' and that would have been that. As it was, I came out about as far as the penalty spot, making it easy for Peter, making sure the ball wouldn't stick in the mud and leave me stranded, when what does he do but come back on it full tilt and belt it past me.

There was nothing I could do, I hadn't even got time to dive. The next thing I knew their players were dancing back to the middle, patting each other on the back, and the whole crowd was laughing – what there was of them. That was a terrible sound, that. All the way around the ground; laughter. And of course you could hear it, that's the terrible thing about a small crowd, that's why, once you get used to it, it's easier to play in front of big ones, because everything gets lost in the general noise. I don't think anything could have made me go back and take that ball out of the net, even if somebody had put a gun in my back. Nothing could make me face those lousy grinning faces that I knew would be there. I could almost feel the laughter, bouncing off my back like a shower of little stones. Peter stared at me and said, 'Well? Aren't you going to get it?' but I shook my head, I didn't say a word.

I knew what he'd think; after all, I was the new boy, and that, but it didn't make any difference. In any case, it was his fault. If he hadn't come dashing in like a lunatic, the way he always seemed to play, always flat out on every tackle, every ball, it never would have happened. So we stood looking at each other for a moment, then he shrugged his shoulders and went and got the ball himself. It was obvious what he felt, that I was making out he'd done it, so he could get it, but though that was true all right, it wasn't the real reason. Anyway, I couldn't have explained.

I thought of my parents up there in the stand, how they'd be feeling, I thought of the lads in the crowd, and I was so sick, I could have turned round and gone off. You get like that sometimes, a goalkeeper; either when someone lets you in for it completely, like he had, or when you're so disgusted with yourself you want to chuck it in. You just have to fight it till it's past; usually after the next save.

Luckily I made one very quickly, and a good one. Their left-forward got up to it well and headed down for my right-hand corner, and I just flung myself as hard as I could for it, got it with my right hand, and turned a somersault, so I didn't know what had happened till Peter patted me on the back and I heard the crowd applauding; a corner. When the corner came over, I came out and got that as well.

Coming back into the goal after clearing, I heard a voice say, 'Very nice, Ron, very nice,' and I didn't even need to look to know who it was; Mike, of course. You could never mistake the tone; like he was patting a dog. I sort of half waved, without looking for him, because it didn't encourage me, it distracted me, it made the crowd too near, too real. From now on, I could feel Mike's eyes on the back of my neck, watching every move I made, and I deliberately came about eight yards out of goal, strolling up and down – we were mostly on the attack – making out I was studying the play, which in fact I was, because that was one way of forgetting myself.

Besides, that was something Reg James had always been very hot on, studying the other side. 'There's two ways of being a goalkeeper,' he used to say. 'You can isolate yourself, or you can be part of the game, and the best goalkeepers are the ones that are part of the game. Doesn't matter how much on top you are, you can always learn something by studying the other side; and your own side. See which foot they like to kick with, their forwards. Which one's liable to get past his man, and what he might do when he does. Which of your own defenders may be off form; and what he's doing wrong. It pays, Ronnie; it always pays.'

In the end, Terry King, our left-winger, put in a couple of goals, one in each half, and we won it pulling away. I noticed that once we were ahead, in fact *before* we were ahead, a lot of the experienced players weren't killing themselves, and in the bath, after the game, there were a lot of sarcastic remarks like, 'Wonder how I'm going to spend the bonus?' which, in the Football Combination, was naturally very small. They were having a bit of a joke with Herbie Brown, too, the second team coach, saying, like, 'Outthought 'em again, eh, Herbie?' or, 'Lost 'em with your tactics, eh, Herb?' the thing being that Herbie, who was really a bit of an old woman, never told you anything much except, 'Keep the ball moving,' or, 'Don't give them room to turn,' things like that. He was another of those that had been with Borough before the war, he'd been a half-back, played for England, and I felt a bit sorry for him, really.

Mind you, he was all right to me, quite encouraging before the game, and afterwards he come up to me and said, 'You did well today, Ronnie,' which was nice. Then when I came out of the dressing-rooms, there was my mother and father, Mary, my sister, and of course Mike and the lads, all saying, 'Well done,' and the rest of it, which was fine, except for the cracks the other players made, like, 'Big name down here, Ronnie,' and, 'Local hero, our Ron.'

Mike was smiling away there, he patted me on the back and said, 'Came back well there, Ronnie, didn't let it upset you.' Then he smiled and nodded at Peter Morton, like he'd known him for years and said, 'Made a game of it, anyway, Peter.' Peter looked at him in a puzzled sort of way and nodded back, as if he couldn't quite place him but reckoned he ought to. Then Mike put his arm round the old man's shoulder and said, 'Good enough start, eh, Mr Blake? Do to be going on with!' and the old man said, 'Yeah, I reckon so, yes,' a bit embarrassed, then we were off to the coach. Mike stood in the road waving, as we went.

In the coach, we sat more or less in two groups, the young ones and the older ones. Us younger ones were quite chuffed at having won and we started singing, 'Can't Buy Me Love', something like that, but the old ones, Bert Coe and the others, started moaning about it, till in the end we stopped. We hadn't got a lot in common, really, even though we were playing in the same team. Even when we talked about something like birds, it was different. Most of them were married with kids and that, you got this feeling that perhaps they envied us a bit, that we could go out chatting up the girls and dancing and the rest, but they all had to wait until their wives weren't looking.

Maybe if we'd had a stronger sort of team manager it might have brought us all together, but Herbie Brown wasn't that kind. It was like one of the younger reserve players said, the right-half, Johnny Elm, 'Staying on for his pension, Herbie is. He's not bothered about anything else.' Except I think he *was*; he was worried about Charlie Macintosh like they all were a bit, all the old coaches, even Reg James, who to me was the best of them; all the coaches that had been with Borough, like Danny once said, since before the Flood.

Anyway, I stayed in the Reserves and although, like I said, the atmosphere wasn't all that, the football was better, you had to be a lot sharper, and it was certainly a promotion. I reckoned it couldn't last that long, because as soon as Harry Vaughan got fit again he'd get back in the League side again, and Terry Morgan would go back into the Reserves. Instead of which, one day I drove down from Borough to Snaresbrook with little Billy Wallis when suddenly he said, 'The other fellow's gone.'

Well, with Billy you had to know what he meant, and it took a bit of time. He hardly ever mentioned anybody by their actual name, unless he was talking to them. It was always 'that bloke', or '*him*', or, 'the other fellow'.

I said, 'Other fellow?'

He said, 'Yes. Gone to Nottingham Forest. £35,000. Quite a lot for a goalkeeper his age.'

And then I cottoned on; I got this feeling coming up in my stomach, like the sun rising or something. I said, 'You mean Harry Vaughan?'

'That's right,' he said, 'Harry. Gone to Forest, hasn't he?'

The rest of the drive I couldn't speak, and since Billy never said much, anyway, we were pretty silent. He did speak, though, he said, when he was going round a roundabout, and getting hooted – he was a funny old driver, Bill, very absent-minded – 'Well, if *he* gets hurt, there's your chance.' This time I didn't have to ask him who he meant, it was obviously Terry Morgan. Then he said one other thing that I remember, just as we were getting near the ground; he said, 'Charlie likes you,' and I got the feeling again. In fact on and off I had it all day, and when I got to bed that night I had it again, stopping me from sleeping. *Charlie likes you* ... Meaning that if Terry got hurt, or maybe if he had a few bad games – I'd be in. In the First Division side. At seventeen. In front of fifty, sixty thousand. It excited me and it scared me a bit, as well. I went to sleep with it, and I woke up with it. In fact from now on I was living with it; this excitement.

Mind you, there was another way of looking at it; that the Boss was going to buy a new keeper, someone he'd put in ahead of Terry *and* me. For all I knew, he was looking for one already, whatever Billy said. Or maybe if Terry threw a few in, in the next four or five matches, he'd say to himself, can't have this, leaving everything down to a seventeen-year-old; then he'd go out and buy. Why I thought he might still be making up his mind was because of the way he and Harry Vaughan had obviously got on one another's wick; he'd flogged Harry because he didn't like him, not to make way for someone else.

In the meantime it was great to be playing in the stiffs every week. For one thing it was quite a lot more money; I used to give it all to my mother every week, and she'd give me back a fiver. The rest went towards the housekeeping, and a few quid into a savings account I'd opened, at the old man's suggestion. Frankly I didn't care a lot about money, not at that time. I was living at home, I hadn't got a car, I was eating once a day at Snaresbrook, I'd buy something new to wear maybe every few weeks – not like Danny who went mad, and was always wearing something different, flared trousers, a kipper tie.

Week by week, too, the Reserve team was getting younger, more and more of my mates were being moved up from the South East Counties League team, out at Acton.

Charlie Macintosh's thing was, he wanted young players; not only in the first team, but in the Reserve team, too. What he said was that if an experienced player wasn't in the first team, there was no point keeping him, because either he was over the top or else, if he was still in the Reserves, he was never going to make it. This was dead against what used to happen at Borough; I heard Herbie Brown and Reg James talk about players in the 'thirties who'd been in the Reserves and played international trials! But to me it made sense; maybe because I was young.

This Terry Morgan was a fair player. He was from somewhere up in Lancashire, about twenty-eight, and he'd been around quite a time. He'd started with Bury, had a few seasons in and out of the first team at Blackpool; I think Charlie Macintosh had signed him because he was short of cover for Harry Vaughan, who'd been first team goalkeeper for about ten years. Now Harry had gone it was a big chance for him, but I don't think it's easy when you've spent so long in Reserve football. I've noticed it a few times; something seems to go, maybe your ambition or something. You're resigned to just coming in for the odd first-team game and picking up your pay at the end of the week. Twenty-eight isn't old for a goalkeeper, but it depends what you've been doing in the meantime.

He was a tall, strong bloke, over six foot, kicked a dead ball a hell of a long way, and got down to the low shots very well, too, for such a big fellow. The only trouble was you never knew what he was going to do. He was one of those goalkeepers who could pull off three or four fabulous saves, then let one dribble in from forty yards. The Boss told the newspapers, 'This is Terry's chance,' and all the rest of it. 'It's up to him, now.' And in fact he started like a bomb, great game at Villa Park, another very good game at home to Everton, and I stopped worrying about would I be in or not. In any case, there wasn't any hurry.

Besides, one morning I turned up at Snaresbrook and there was Danny, large as life and grinning all over his face. He said, 'Caught you up, haven't I?' We played a practice game that morning and he looked fantastic, pulling the ball back with the sole of his boot, 'nutmegging' people by pushing it between their legs, spraying it around all over the place. Driving me back to Borough afterwards, Billy Wallis said, 'He can play a bit, old Lofty,' which was about the best you ever heard him say about anybody. 'Lot of confidence, too, hasn't he?'

That Saturday, Danny was in the Combination side. We went down to Bristol Rovers, it was a wet day, a very heavy pitch, but he strolled around like he always did and got the only goal, after he'd walked round a couple of defenders and sent the goalkeeper the wrong way. I was very pleased for him, but I don't think some of the older players were too happy. They didn't like the way he went on; you could tell that. They thought he was cocky.

One afternoon, when I suppose Danny had been in the Reserve team three or four weeks, him and I and a few of the others were up at Borough, in the treatment room; we'd all got knocks of one kind or another. I forget what I had, bruised elbow I think it was. Danny was on the table getting the old ultra-sonics from Sid Grayne, the second-team trainer, a quiet sort of bloke, another that had been at Borough nearly all his life. Suddenly the phone rang in the room; Sid picked it up, gave it to Danny and said, 'It's for you.'

Danny took it and said, 'Yeah?' very casual like he always was, he didn't even get up off his stomach. Then he started getting interested, he said, 'Yeah, okay ... Fine ... How much? Twenty quid? ... Yeah! That'll be great,' then he give the phone back to Sid. Peter Morton was in the room, he asked, 'Who was that, then, Danny?' and Danny said, like it was the kind of thing that happened to him every day, 'Oh, just a reporter that wants to interview me.'

'Interview *you*,' said Peter, 'Why? What have *you* done?'

'Promising stars,' Danny says. 'Some evening paper up North. He's doing a series.'

Well, all us younger ones in the room, there was two or three of us, got a bit envious at that. 'Oh,' says Peter, 'you're a promising star, are you?' and Sid says, rubbing away at Danny's thigh, 'They're getting younger and younger, aren't they?'

'Making me feel old, Sid,' Peter says, and Danny says, 'You *are* old, Peter; no offence,' but Peter doesn't take it bad, he just asks, 'Where are you meeting him?'

Danny says, 'Great Western Hotel tonight, at six,' which sounded the right sort of place, because a lot of football people stay there. 'Put in a word for me, Dan,' Peter says, 'what did he offer you? Twenty quid?' and Danny says, 'That's right,' still very, very casual.

'Money for nothing,' Peter says, 'wish I could pick up money like that,' and Sid says, 'Don't know how lucky they are, this generation.'

Next morning Danny turns up at Snaresbrook and he looks like he's really choked. I said, 'All right, then, Danny? How's it go? Get your twenty quid?' but he just muttered something and walked away. After training, in the dressing-rooms, the others, some of the older second-team players, started asking him things, how'd it gone, what was he going to do with the money, but Danny didn't answer, he was very quiet in the bath, till in the end while he was knotting his tie he said, 'The burke didn't turn up.'

'What?' says Peter, 'didn't turn up? After all that line he gave you?' Danny said, 'Sat there from six till bleeding ten. Never heard a dicky-bird. Next time he rings me up, I'll tell him he can get stuffed.'

And at that very moment, Bert Coe looked in and said, 'Danny? Wanted on the phone! Says he's a reporter,' and I'd never seen Danny move quicker than he did then, out of the bath. He came back a few minutes later with a towel round him, looking a lot more cheerful and he said, throwing it away like, 'It was the same bloke.'

'Oh, yes?' says Terry King. 'I thought you weren't ever going to speak to him again!'

'He got held up,' Danny said, 'his taxi was caught in the traffic. He says he turned up five minutes after I'd left.'

'Going to meet him again, then?' Peter Morton asked him, and Danny said yes he was, same place, Great Western Hotel, only this time it was going to be at seven, so they could have supper. Peter said, 'Maybe he'll only be two minutes late, this time.'

Well, to cut a long story short, it went on like this for three or four days, Danny getting these telephone calls from this reporter, making appointments all the time, and either the bloke not turning up at all, or phoning through to say he couldn't make it. Till in the end he made a date with him at the Great Northern Hotel, the other one, over at King's Cross, quite near the Borough ground, but this time when Danny got there he found about four of the Reserve team waiting for him, the older ones, Peter Morton, Bert Coe, Terry King, and a couple of others. One of them was Gerry Ford the left-half, who was quite good at these impersonations. I was told Danny took one look at them, swore, and just turned and walked out. It was a long time before he heard the end of that one.

Being Danny, though, he didn't take it lying down. Things started happening to them; like one day one of them might find his boots full of muddy water when he came to put them on; or another time he came up to Bert Coe and said, 'Congratulations, Bert, hear your wife's just had a baby,' and handed him a bottle of champagne which ... well anyway, it wasn't champagne. I couldn't have done it, but you couldn't keep Danny down.

Besides, he knew he had the Boss on his side. Now and again they'd have a bit of a barney in a practice game when the Boss was playing, and Danny would nutmeg him or sell him a dummy, but Charlie Macintosh thought a lot of him, he was always praising him in the practices, saying to the others, 'Now, that's the way to trap a ball,' or, 'Look how he gets up to it.' Personally, I was glad for Danny, but you could see some of the others didn't like it too much.

As for me, it was still going well. All the young players coming up into the Reserves made the atmosphere a lot different, all trying hard, all wanting to win, all of us with something to play for. Especially me, because I reckoned that if I went on doing well, the Boss would carry on as things were, without going out to buy another goalkeeper, a more experienced one.

One Saturday we'd been playing at Coventry. We drew 1–1; it wasn't a very good game. They had one of those Reserve sides that were always hard for a young team like us to play against; full of players who'd played a lot in the

League side and never made it. They probably weren't going to get any better now, but they still had the edge on us in terms of experience. Teams like that were inclined to put it about a bit, too; they didn't like getting shown up by young players, especially ones like Danny, who were always liable to make you look stupid, make you dive in for the ball, then find it wasn't there. I heard Billy Wallis say to him once, 'Want to watch that, Danny.'

Danny said, 'Watch what?' He respected Billy, although he was such a funny little quiet fellow, because he reckoned he could play. In fact he often got Billy to show him tricks he did, that he wanted to copy, himself.

Billy said, 'You'll get yourself kicked to death, the way you're going, son. Beat 'em, but don't make a fool of 'em. Not of a professional.' Most people, Danny would have given an argument, Danny always liked to be right, and even with Billy he didn't agree, he just nodded and said nothing, but you could see he was thinking about it.

Anyway, we got to the railway station and we all bought the football edition of the local evening paper, the Pink 'Un, the Green 'Un, whatever it was. We knew the first team had gone down 3–1 at Sunderland, when suddenly Peter Morton called out, 'Here! Terry Morgan got done! Carried off on a stretcher! Alf Curtis had to go in goal!'

Well, when I heard that, I stopped dead in my tracks. It was like somebody had run an electric shock through me. I can't say I felt pleased, I can't say I felt frightened, I just had this shock. One of the other lads said, 'Poor old Terry. Wonder what happened to him?' and everybody started fingering through their papers to the page where the report was, just a few lines of it. It didn't say what he'd done; just that he'd been in a collision with one of their forwards.

I sat in a corner in the dining car, opposite Danny, not saying anything, till at last he looked at me smiling and said, 'Think you'll be in then, Ronnie?'

'Me?' I said. 'In where?'

'Come off it!' he said. 'Who're they going to put in if Terry's out?'

'He may not be out,' I said. 'You don't know. He may be okay by Saturday. It could just be bruising, or something.'

'What, carried off on a stretcher?' Danny says. 'Just for bruising?'

'You don't know, do you?' I said. 'Not until he's had an X-ray.'

But Danny wasn't going to let me go, now. He called to Herbie Brown, who was coming past just then. 'Hey, Herbie! Ron'll be in next week, won't he? Certainty!' This was done to kid Herbie, as well, because everybody knew how cautious he was, never wanting to leave himself open, never saying anything until he knew how the Boss felt about it. He said, 'I don't know. I don't pick the first team, do I? Besides, how do you know Terry Morgan won't be fit?' and Danny said, 'You must be joking!'

Then he winked across the table at Ralph Plumb, a young Geordie boy who had just got into the Reserves at right-back, and he said, 'Who've the first team got next week, Ralph?'

Ralph said, 'Liverpool, isn't it?'

Danny winked again, I caught him, and he asked, 'What, home or away?' though I could tell he knew.

Ralph said, 'Away, I think,' very serious, he was always a quiet, serious sort of lad, he wasn't really joining him in the joke. But that really set Danny off, he said, 'Well, that's a debut for you, eh, Ronnie? In front of the Kop! That's a bit of an old ordeal!' Which made me feel as if I hadn't got no stomach, because we all knew about the Kop, the noise they made behind the goal, the songs and the chants, the way they could give a visiting player stick if they didn't like him. And what would that be like for a goalkeeper, who'd have to stand there and take it for a whole forty-five minutes?

'I'd be injured as well if I was you, Ronnie,' Danny says.

'Got a knock in the second half today, didn't you? Bad, that. Didn't like the look of it at the time. You saw him get that knock, didn't you, Ralph? I was amazed he played on. Man of iron.'

Herbie Brown called across, 'All right, Danny, that's enough; you don't want to go worrying the lad.'

'Me?' says Danny, shooting up his eyebrows. 'Worry him? Nerves of steel this kid's got. Honestly, Mr Brown. Seventeen years old and cool as a veteran. You could put him in there, Kop or no Kop, and he wouldn't turn a hair.'

'You would,' said Bert Coe, who didn't like him. 'You'd crease yourself.'

Then the conversation changed, but I must say I didn't join in too much, I didn't eat much. I'd got the Kop on my mind.

When I got back that night I'd got a date with a girl; we went to a cinema. Saturday nights, that was what I usually did; I wanted to unwind, I felt tired – even if there hadn't been a lot to do, there's the strain – and I wouldn't fancy going dancing. Sundays I'd go in for that; if there was a good discothèque open.

That night, though, I didn't notice the film much. I was running my own film, a film of the Kop; like I'd seen it on telly, anyway. The songs and the chants and all the scarves waving; 'You'll Never Walk Alone', and all the rest of it. And I prayed that if I *did* play, because I was really torn about playing, we'd be attacking the Kop end the first half, so I wouldn't have to face it till the second, when maybe I'd have played myself in.

The girl who was with me got a bit narked, she kept asking me, 'What's the matter, Ron? You tired, or something?' I told her, 'No, I'm not tired,' but I didn't say anything else. I mean, how could you explain to a bird?

Next morning, I was waiting on the doorstep for the Sunday papers to arrive. I'd only slept a few hours. When I did I had dreams; in one of them I was keeping goal at Anfield,

70

in front of the Kop – I knew I was at Liverpool, although there wasn't any noise or anything – and this ball was trickling slowly, slowly past me, over the line. I was on the ground; I kept trying to get up and stop it, it was only a yard or so away, but every time I tried, I couldn't make it, something seemed to hold me back. A terrible dream, that was.

When the papers came, I was trembling so much I could hardly open them, in fact I dropped them. Then I picked one up, and as soon as I turned to the back page, there it was in big black letters, all the way across the top: BOROUGH GOALKEEPER BREAKS ARM. Apparently he'd dived at the fellow's feet, he was always very brave, and the bloke had followed through and kicked him. The paper said that he'd be out for weeks. I went back inside the flat very, very slowly; and in fact that was how the whole day passed; slowly.

At breakfast, I didn't even mention what had happened, for some reason I thought it would be unlucky. At last the old man saw it, he said, 'Coo! Seen this, Ronnie? Terry Morgan broke his arm.' I sort of mumbled something, and he said, 'This could be your chance, then, Ronnie.'

I said, 'Yeah, yeah, it could,' and my mother and my sister were all beaming at me, and the old man got very excited, what a wonderful thing it would be, of course he was sorry about the way it had happened, and all that stuff.

'You can't be sure,' I said. 'He might go out and buy another goalkeeper. I mean, I'm seventeen, aren't I?'

'No, he won't,' says Dad. 'He'd never do that, not with the opinion he's got of you. Remember what he said? He said you'd play for England by the time you're twenty-one!'

'Yeah, I know,' I said, 'but that's a long way off, isn't it? That's nearly four years' time. Besides, he may not fancy slipping me in at Liverpool.'

'Liverpool?' says the old man. 'Well, that's a test, isn't

it? That's a hard one, son. That's jumping in the deep end.'
I didn't need him or anyone to tell me that.

Monday, I drove down from Borough with little Billy Wallis, like I always did, and I was just bursting to ask him, what'll happen, will I be in, how do you think I'll do, only that wasn't the way with Billy, this was something you learned. Ask him a direct question and you'd get nowhere; you had to wait till it came out of him in hints, sort of thrown away.

We talked a bit about the Sunderland game, how we hadn't been good, we'd been 2–1 down at the time Terry Morgan got carried off, and not really looking like coming back.

Then, as if he'd read what I was thinking, he suddenly came out and said, 'Wouldn't be worth buying another keeper not now. Mid-season; no chance of the title, no danger of going down.' And I realized what he was telling me; that I was bound to be in, they wouldn't go looking for anybody else, at least not for the moment. In fact the next thing he said was, which was obviously connected, though at first it didn't seem so, was, 'Hear you done well again at Coventry, Ron.'

All that week, though, the Boss didn't say a word, though once he took me himself for special training. Pressure training, it was, he was very keen on that. He wasn't that keen on the old Football Association coaching methods, though he'd been on courses and he'd got the badge; he'd point at it sometimes, winking, and he'd say, 'There's my passport. There's my credentials. Twenty-five years in the game; useless! You've *no* chance without the badge!' But one thing he did believe in was this pressure training, ball after ball after ball coming at you, whether it was people hitting crosses or him throwing them at you and making you get up and down to them on the ground, till you were right nackered.

He'd never taken me for as long as he did this time,

though; and to me, that meant something, too. In fact most of the others seemed to take it for granted I'd be playing at Anfield. Danny kept taking the mickey. He'd put one past me when they were shooting in, and call out, 'Left foot drive . . . and just listen to the Kop!'

On Friday, we did what we always did, turned up at Borough instead of Snaresbrook to look at the team lists; then we'd get paid, go into the gym, and maybe do some training on the all-weather area.

Naturally the first thing I did was go to the team sheets. All the way there, on the tube, I tried not to think about it, tried to read the paper, tried looking at the advertisements, tried looking at the birds; no use. What else was there to think about? The night before, the evening paper had had a piece, 17-YEAR-OLD KEEPER IN LINE FOR LEAGUE DEBUT, how I was the obvious choice now Terry Morgan was hurt, but Charlie Macintosh wouldn't give the team till Friday. Apparently all he'd say was, 'Ronnie has been show-ing good form in the Reserves,' which to me could have meant anything.

All the way up to the ground from the station my heart was thumping like I'd been running up and down the ter-races, and those steps in front of the main entrance were like Everest. I didn't even get to the notice boards before Tommy Dougall, the first team inside-left, came up to me and clapped me on the shoulder and said, 'You're in, son; congratulations!' and then they were all coming round me, clapping me on the back, wishing me good luck, saying, 'Keep 'em out, Ronnie! Make a name, son!' I felt a bit dazed, and the funny thing was that when I came out of it, all I could think of was, I've got no clothes with me; we'll be staying up in Liverpool, and I've brought no things. Then Billy Wallis came up and said, 'The Boss wants to see you, Ronnie. Told you you'd be in, didn't I?'

I said, 'Yes; yes, you did,' and it was only when I was halfway up the stairs to the Boss's office that I realized that he never had, not directly. I supposed that was Billy's way of telling.

The Boss was in a suit, for once. He popped up behind his desk, shook hands with me, told me to sit down, and said, 'Don't let *me* down, and I won't let *you* down. Play well at Liverpool, and you'll stay in.'

I suppose I just sort of gaped at him, I didn't know what to say, and he went on. 'You can do it all right. You've got the temperament. You've got the physique. Age doesn't matter any more. Age is not important. Kids these days grow up so quick. Are you worried about it being Liverpool? Worried about the Kop?'

'Well,' I said, 'I think I'd rather have had it here.'

'Nonsense!' he said. 'Couldn't be better. There's less pressure on away from home, and the Kop's a wonderful crowd. They'll help you. They'll encourage you. Make one good save early on, and they'll all be on your side.'

That started to cheer me up; it was something that I'd never thought of. Then he said, 'You're the goalkeeper for me. I'd have liked to hold you back a few more months, but it doesnae matter. This Morgan will never be a keeper. Keep out two, throw in three. He's too old to improve.'

Then he told me he'd ring home and send for my things. He said, 'This is how I like to do it. I didn't want you worrying all the week,' which was a bit odd, seeing what I'd been through, but I supposed I saw his point. Just as I went out, he called, 'And move your gear into the first-team dressing-room.'

After training, they slung me into the bath with my tracksuit on, like they did to all new first team players. I didn't mind; I don't think I'd have minded if I'd even had my newest suit on, with the flared trousers and the long jacket. Though of course what I put on afterwards was the club blazer and flannels like everybody else; a bit square, but who cared? It was what Terry Morgan once said: 'You

74

don't mind putting them on. It's like a uniform, like joining a crack regiment.'

Sitting on the coach on the way to the railway station, I felt like I was up on a cloud. Everything somehow looked different; the streets, the dirty old houses, even the people in the streets. Now and again they'd glance up at the coach and nudge one another and nod towards it, recognizing it; Borough United. Sometimes I thought they were looking straight at me, though of course they couldn't have been; pointing and saying, 'That's the new one. That's the boy that's going to play in goal.'

The Boss was sitting a few seats in front of me, next to Billy Wallis. He turned round and smiled at me and said, 'How's it feel to be a first-team player, Ronnie?'

'Great, Boss,' I said, 'great,' and one of the lads called out, 'Ask him tomorrow evening, Boss. Ask him when we come away from Anfield.' The Boss said, 'He'll feel greater still. You wait and see,' and another of them sang, 'Now I'm a believer!'

Quite a few of them were already playing cards; aces and kings, which was the popular game in our club, then. Myself, I'd never played cards much before, I didn't go a lot on gambling, but what I found was that on away trips you had to do something, or you'd go crazy. All those hours and hours in trains, and later on, on plane trips. All that hanging about in hotels with nothing to do, not allowed to go out on the town. Tommy Dougall, who was sitting next to me, was reading a book, some paperback. He'd had more schooling than most of us and he certainly read more; he certainly talked more, too, but he'd sometimes join in the cards school, too.

When we got to the station, there was a crowd of kids wearing Borough scarves hanging about at the entrance of the platform, with autograph books, albums and that. Three or four of them came up to me and said, 'Sign,

Ronnie! Good luck, Ronnie! See you don't let none through, Ron!' and it was a funny feeling to think that not all that long ago, I might have been doing what they were.

What surprised me was the pictures they already had of me that they wanted me to sign, some that I'd never seen before, me diving, me going up to catch a ball; pictures from I don't know where. Anyway, I signed them, then we all got on the train.

First-class seats; that was something new, as well. I'd stayed up North with the youth team a few times, but we'd always gone second. This was different, though; compartments all to ourselves, 'Reserved for Borough United F.C.' on the windows, lovely plush blue seats to lean back on. I think the Boss must have guessed what I was thinking when I sat down, because he smiled at me and said, 'Better than cycling, isn't it?'

A card game was still going on in our compartment; in fact it was under way before the train even moved. I remember how much I envied the lads at the time, how they could get into a coach on the way up to a big match and right away get out the cards, transfer to a railway carriage and pull them straight out again, as if they'd never moved. They asked me would I join in, and I did after they'd played a couple of hands, but I was very distracted, and when I'd lost a couple of quid I pulled out of it and read the paper; or I tried to. What I'd rather have done was sleep, like another of the lads, the twelfth man, Wally Evans, was doing in the corner; in fact I envied him even more than the ones that could settle down to cards.

One of the boys looked across at him and said, 'There he goes already, old Kipper,' which was his nickname. 'He'd sleep if you hung him upside down from a tree.'

At Liverpool, there were more kids on the station, a few of them, wearing red and white Liverpool scarves, asking us to sign. One of them said to me, in that Scouse accent of theirs, 'Give us a goal, Ronnie,' but the Boss, who was following up behind, said, 'A thick ear more like, son.'

Our hotel was in the middle of Liverpool, the biggest I'd ever stayed at in England; great, big lounges, springy carpets, and lots of marble. I suppose I must have been looking around a bit, because one of the others said, 'Come on, Ron; it ain't no blinking palace!' They were all strolling in like they did it every week; which, of course, they more or less did.

I was put in a room with Graham Gibbs, the right-half, a very nice lad from Portsmouth, always happy and friendly, only a couple of years older than myself. He'd just played for England Under 23 and he was on top of the world then. He was a good player, Graham, a good, hard grafter in midfield who could go through and hit a ball, too, especially with his right foot. He was very good with me, trying to help me relax, telling me what this one and that one did in the Liverpool team; what I'd have to look out for.

He said, 'You want to watch Peter Thompson; he's got this habit of cutting it from the left, then pivoting to hit it with his right. Remember he's two-footed; two very, very powerful feet. Then look out for Steve Heighway, breaking from half-way. He's very fast, he'll push it by the centre-half and go. But if you anticipate it, you can be out of your area, to kick it clear.' Things like that; I was grateful.

While I was up in the room, there was a call from London; some reporter on the *Daily Mail*. I was a bit leery about taking it at first, I remembered what they'd all done to Danny; I told Graham, 'They ain't catching me,' and I told the fellow, into the phone, 'How do I know you're from the *Daily Mail*? How do I know you're not just having me on?' and he sounded a bit choked, he said, 'Well, I can't show you my Press card over the telephone, can I?' Graham asked me who the bloke was; I told him the name, he took the phone from me, and he talked to him, then he gave it back to me and said, 'It's all right, Ron; this bloke's genuine.'

So then came all these questions; was I nervous? How did I feel about playing in front of the Kop? Would I be doing anything for luck? I told him no, I wasn't nervous, because that would look good, wouldn't it; RONNIE BLAKE SAYS I'M SHAKING. As for the things that bring me luck, or that *I* think bring me luck, I never tell them to anyone, because although it may sound silly, to me, once you tell somebody, they won't work; if they ever did.

There were a couple of other phone calls after that, and I answered the questions in the same way. Later when I got back to London and the family showed me what they'd put in the London papers, a right load of old codswallop, how I was raring to face the Kop, it had always been my ambition to play there, and all that, I wondered why they'd bothered to speak to me at all. It was all right, it didn't really matter, it didn't do any harm, but this was my first experience of the papers, and I can tell you, there was a lot worse to come.

We ate quite early that evening, then we went out to the pictures; it was a cowboy film. Normally I like them, but this one, I couldn't tell you anything about it. I wasn't seeing cowboys, I was seeing centre-forwards, and those guns weren't firing bullets, they were firing footballs.

When we got back, the trainer, Don Collins, asked me did I want a sedative. He said, 'We don't encourage them, but I talked to the doc before we came away; he said it wouldn't do you any harm, before a match like that.' I thought about it a moment, then I refused; I'd never taken pills like that in my life and I was afraid to start it now; what if it had a bad effect? That'd be nice, if I didn't sleep all night, then lay down and fell asleep in the goal. So I said no; I'd try and do without one.

And I didn't sleep. Well, hardly. It was another of those

nights; only this one got desperate. I just *had* to sleep; I knew that. How could I play if I was dead tired?

Luckily they let you sleep on the morning of away games; I got off some time or other, and when I woke up, I felt lost, I didn't know where I was for a moment, I was really scared. Just in those few moments before, of course, I realized; Liverpool, the hotel bedroom. The match. And that sparked off another right panic; what was the time, where was Graham? They'd kicked off without me, they'd had to play without a goalkeeper; I can't tell you what went through my head, just in these few seconds. I even had a picture of me coming on in the middle of the game in my green jersey, and the whole crowd, the Kop and everybody, taking the mickey.

The curtains were still drawn, and at first I couldn't find the light switch. I panicked again, I jumped out of bed and tore back the curtains, without bothering about the cords. When I looked at my watch, it said twenty to eleven, but the next thing come into my head was maybe it had stopped. I put it to my ear and it hadn't, it was still going. Then I saw the telephone, between the beds; I picked it up and asked them what the time was, and they told me; twenty to eleven. It was okay.

There was a bathroom next to the room; our own. That was something, too. A hotel room with a bathroom. Lovely big white, soft towels, taps that shone like they'd been polished that morning, a shower over the bath; the lot. I was in the bath, running it very hot, beginning to feel a bit better, when I heard someone come in the room. I called, 'Graham?' and it was. I told him, 'I thought I'd overslept.' He said, 'You did, but I left you to it. Want any breakfast?'

I said, 'Yeah, I'll come down.' He said, 'No need to come down.' I said, 'What; up here?' and he laughed at me, he said, 'Yes. You could have had it in bed if you wanted. Waitresses are a bit over the top, though.' So I said fine, yes, I'd have it in the room; this was wonderful, this, this was living. While I was shaving, Graham went through the Liverpool attack again; he also warned me about Emlyn Hughes, coming through from midfield and shooting from twenty-five yards or so, right-footed. In fact by the time he was finished he had me feeling like I'd be facing a kind of firing squad. I know he meant it well, he meant to help, but believe me, he didn't.

When I went downstairs, I wandered into the big sitting-room they had, and there were a couple of card schools going. Little Billy Wallis come up to me and said, 'All right, Ronnie?' I said, 'Yeah, not too bad.'

He said, 'Sleep all right, did you?' and I said, 'Okay,' not wanting to tell him, in case he said I should have had the sleeping pill; but he had a look at me and I reckon he could see, all right. Then he asked me, 'Got butterflies?' I told him, 'No; not yet,' and he said, 'Don't worry if they come; I always had them. Right to the end. So did Stanley Matthews. Know what he used to say? "You've got to have butterflies." People that don't feel nothing; well, they're never players. If every match is just the same, Cup or League, international or a friendly, then you'll never raise your game, will you?'

'I don't know,' I said. 'Maybe there are people who always play well; any game.'

'No,' he said, 'there never are. There can't be. Especially goalkeepers. A keeper's like, I don't know, a sort of trapeze artist. Maybe like a singer, an entertainer; if he's any good. You know; something special. He's got to be keyed up to be good. It stands to reason.'

We sat down and he ordered some coffee. It was like waiting for a war to begin. A little bloke came over and joined us, he was the correspondent from the local weekly paper, in London; he followed Borough everywhere; I'd met him once or twice and he'd always been very nice, which was another thing. Some reporters that I'd come across would just give you hallo and good-bye, down at

Snaresbrook and places, as if to say you weren't worth wasting their time on. His name was Doug Green, this little fellow, and he seemed to get on very well with Billy, they'd obviously been mates a long time. Billy said to me, 'Doug's all right, Ron; Doug won't let you down,' and then Doug started asking me questions, dozens of them, writing them down in a notebook in shorthand. Where did I go to school, where was I born, how did I become a goalkeeper, when did I first play in the Combination team, what keepers did I admire, and when I told him Peter Bonetti, Billy winked and said, 'You don't want to tell him that, Ron. That's sabotage, that is.' But the little bloke wrote it down and said, 'No, no, that's very interesting, very interesting indeed.' He seemed very serious, very conscientious, and he kept talking about Borough players I'd never heard of, goalkeepers who'd done this, that, and the other before the war. Even Billy didn't seem to remember some of them.

At the end, Billy said to him, 'Well, you got enough to write a book about him now, Doug,' and the little bloke said, 'This is only chapter one, Billy. I hope there'll be many others.' Then he shook hands with me and wished me luck; it was something I remembered for a long time. I think young players do remember things like that; most of them. Though much later on, when I mentioned it to Doug Green, he shook his head, very sad, and said, 'Ah, you'd be surprised, Ronnie, the ones that walk past you. You're one of the exceptions.'

Billy and I and a few of the others went out for a walk, then; just to stretch our legs and get the air, there certainly wasn't much to see in Liverpool. Great, big, ugly stone buildings looming over everything. The main thing I noticed was the rain, sort of a light drizzle, the kind that worries you because you don't know whether you ought to wear your gloves or not. The other lads were very nice, obviously trying to take my mind off things, laughing and joking a lot. Billy asked me would my people be coming up for the game, but I said no, I knew the old man was working that afternoon. He did every other Saturday. In a way I was disappointed, in another I was pleased. It was bad enough facing the Kop.

Charlie Macintosh talked about that again when we had the team talk, just before lunch. He said if we played well the Kop would applaud us, which was the great thing about playing at Anfield, how he'd always enjoyed it when he was playing for the Wolves, because they'd had this kind of duel. They always called him, 'Dirty Macintosh,' and sang these songs at him, 'Ee-ay-addey-oh, Macintosh is a thug,' but there was nothing in it; if he did a good tackle, they'd appreciate it. Then he ran through the Liverpool team, saying more or less what Graham had said, only not laying it on quite so thick about the shooting, and ended up saying he wished me luck and he was sure everybody else did, but if he'd had any doubts about me, I wouldn't have been here.

Some of the directors were there at lunch. Steak and toast for us, though not for them; I noticed they had bottles of wine on the table, they were having a right old guzzle. To me, seeing them together that first time, they all looked the same; big, fat men with red faces, who looked as if they did themselves well and did it often. In fact Bob Cullen our centre-forward, he was an Ipswich boy, looked over at them and said, 'Snouts in the trough, again.' They all of them worked in the City, and I must say they looked like it, though the lads said that the Chairman, who was a little bit slimmer than the others – which wasn't saying a lot – was quite a decent bloke; he understood the game a bit, and he looked after the players. What they didn't like was the hangers-on, but I didn't see them till on the coach that evening after the game. They were like the directors only even bigger and redder, and they made more noise.

In the coach out to Anfield, I sat next to Graham Gibbs. I hoped he wouldn't run through the Liverpool attack again and what they'd do, but this time thank goodness he didn't. Now and again we'd pass little groups of Liverpool fans in their scarves, going to the game, and if they noticed us, they'd wave their arms at us and hold up fingers to show three–nil or five–nil, what they thought they were going to beat us by. Most of the lads ignored it, one or two smiled and waved back, but it was all in fun and nobody was bothered by it.

A miserable place it looked to me, driving through the streets, never mind the Mersey Sound and all the rest of it. I said to Graham, 'No wonder the Beatles came to London.' In the dressing-room, there was plenty of time to get ready; too much, really. I tried to spin out the getting stripped as long as I possibly could, but just the same, I was one of the first ready. Naturally I put my right boot on first, but after that, to be quite honest, the thing that was really worrying me was, could I be last but one out on the field?

In the Reserves, it had always been okay. There were one or two wanted to be last, and what they did was take it in turns, or otherwise come out side by side, though it sometimes meant a bit of a squeeze if you had a narrow tunnel. But up here, with the first team, I just didn't know, and I was too nervous to ask. Billy came up to me while I was sitting there and asked was there anything wrong, he said, 'Is it the old butterflies?' I said no, no, it wasn't that. In fact they came on later, and I wished he hadn't reminded me.

I said to him, 'I'll be okay as soon as we get out there, Bill; as soon as we start playing,' but he could see there was still something wrong, and in the end he had it out of me, I said, 'Well, it's when I come out. You know. What position,' and he understood right away, having been a player himself, he knew what a thing like that could mean. He asked, 'Where do you normally come out?'

I said, 'Last but one,' and he said, 'Well, that ain't no problem. There's Ray McGraw always likes to come out last, Tommy Dougall likes to come out second, and Arthur Prescott, he doesn't mind as long as he *isn't* last. Don't worry about that, Ron. I'll have a word with Jack Noakes,' which was the skipper.

I saw him talking to Jack, and Jack nodding; it was a hell of a relief, I can tell you. He was a queer bloke, Jack. A Stepney boy, only twenty-one or so, and the thing about him was, he never showed any emotion. Never; no matter what happened. He could put through his own goal at a vital stage of the match, and you still wouldn't see him turn a hair, there'd still be no reaction. Mind you, he'd smile when we scored, I'll give him that, but then I reckon anybody would, they could hardly stop it. The other thing was, fouls. He was a left-half, stopper, and he was very, very hard. I've seen him do some wicked things.

There were times when it made you laugh a bit, this poker faced expression of his, especially after he'd chopped somebody. He'd just sort of fade away then, and the next thing you know he'd be ten or fifteen yards off looking up at the sky, all innocent, like it hadn't got anything to do with him.

Billy spoke to him, I saw him shrugging and shaking his head, then Billy came back and told me, 'Jack says that's fine with him; he don't mind at all.' In fact you never saw Jack open his mouth much, except when something went wrong in the defence, then he opened it so wide I sometimes thought he'd get lockjaw, shouting and carrying on at people in a way you'd never think he was capable of. Tommy Dougall used to call him Dr Jackie and Mr Noakes. As a captain, he never really did a lot; I mentioned it to Tommy Dougall once and he said, 'That's why he's captain.'

There'd been a time, when Charlie Macintosh arrived at the club, when Bert Coe was skipper, but that only lasted about a season. Charlie liked giving the orders, as I found. He didn't encourage a lot of discussion, not even at team conferences, but with a young team, there wasn't that much back chat, anyway.

Then it was time to go out. The longest, slowest walk of my life, that was, Charlie Macintosh stood at the door of the dressing-room, shaking hands with each one of us in turn as we went by. Liverpool went out first and there was this tremendous roar, it stopped you in your tracks. Then it was us, and I tucked myself in behind Jack Noakes. He said, 'All right, lads, we'll show the Kop,' and out we went.

Trotting on to the pitch, behind Jack, I didn't look up at first, I just let the sound sort of batter off me. Thank heaven we didn't go to the Kop end; it was Liverpool always kicked in there, anyway. I got in the other goal, Arthur Prescott and Joe Lyons, the two full-backs, stood on the posts, and the lads started shooting in. Bob Cullen lobbed me a nice easy one, that I caught above my head, then Jesse Maude, the right-winger, put over a cross that I came out and caught. I punched out one or two shots that were coming straight at me, let one or two in that weren't worth diving for, and by the time we'd done, I reckoned I had the feel of the ball.

Jack Noakes went trotting off to the middle to toss up, and now I took my first look up the other end; at the Kop. What surprised me was that it wasn't taller. I'd expected it to be towering up, like some kind of cliff, but it didn't, it was fairly low. There was a lot of noise coming from there, the 'Ee-ay-addey-oh' stuff, and all the rest of it, a lot of red-and-white scarves waving, but it didn't overawe you; not the sight of it, anyway.

Jack Noakes won the toss, thank goodness, and said we'd attack the Kop goal. When I saw him making as if to push us back with his hands, meaning, 'As we are,' I was really chuffed.

So Liverpol kicked off, and within a minute I'd had to make a save; the best start I could ever have hoped for. The ball went down the right-wing to Callaghan, he crossed it,

85

an outswinger, and I could see it wasn't going to be a goal-keeper's ball. At the same time, I reckoned that Ray Mc-Graw, our centre-half, had gone a bit too far over to the left; which left John Toshack with a chance of getting it, because he could see it, too. He hadn't gone with Ray, to challenge him, he was waiting, and I knew what he could do with that head of his, even without being told by Graham and the Boss.

Sure enough, Ray went up for the cross and couldn't quite make contact. Toshack jumped and headed it down low, on the bounce, for my left-hand corner; back the way it had come. But being on my line, I was able to fling myself; I just got a hand to it and had it round the post. Then they were thumping me on the back, Jackie Noakes, Joe Lyons, and Ray McGraw. Ray said, 'Thanks, Ronnie; I'll get the corner away for you,' and he did, he got up to it well, he headed it out to the right.

I felt good, then; I'd got right into the game, like you do when you make an early save. There wasn't going to be any standing about in the cold, waiting for something to happen. In fact very soon something else *did* happen. Emlyn Hughes, I think it was, hit a long ball down the middle, and Steve Heighway came after it like a bomb; he had about a yard on Ray McGraw, Joe Lyons was cutting across from the left, but I could see that he was never going to make it. On the other hand, going that fast, Heighway didn't have it under full control. After what I'd been told, I'd been ready for something like this, I was watching for it the moment that ball was hit. I knew it was no good staying in my area, I'd be done for, so I came out as fast as I could and just beat him to it. I belted it right-footed into the crowd. The boys were very pleased about that one, too.

The rest of the half we took control a bit, at any rate in midfield. We were playing more of a 4-4-2, really, than a 4-3-3, with little Jesse Maude, our Geordie winger, coming back a lot. He was a great little runner, Jesse; he'd always go until he dropped. The other thing was we'd got a couple of very good ball-holding players in Harry Jackson, who was a London boy from Streatham, and Tommy Dougall. Tommy was often criticized for hanging on too long, not letting go till everyone was picked up, but in a situation like this, it can be a good thing, it gives the team confidence in itself. The only thing that worried me a bit was he might overdo it, get tackled on the edge of the box or something, then they could come away with the man over, and have us in dead trouble.

Generally, though, all there was to do was catch a few crosses, although it was nothing like as easy as in the Reserve team. Here, you had people really going up with you, pressurizing you, especially this Toshack. A ball would come over, you'd think, 'Mine, easy,' but when you went for it, you'd be amazed; there was somebody's nut there, with you. Usually, like I say, Toshack's. He could certainly climb a bit; besides being tall.

About five minutes from half-time, we suddenly came away and scored; and in a way, I started it. Jack Noakes pushed a ball back to me, I rolled it to the edge of the area and picked it up, but when I looked around, there was nobody to throw it to, everyone was marked. The only thing to do was kick it, which I did; not up the middle, where they'd got this big, tall centre-half, Larry Loyd, getting everything, but out to the left-wing, where I could see Jesse.

He was only a little fellow, but he gets up well, and he backheaded it into the middle. Bob Cullen laid it off right away, and Ernie Leech went through like a tank, dodged between a couple of them, and hit it past Ray Clemence. I was dancing about in the goalmouth like a lunatic; I heard someone yell out from behind the goal, 'Take him away! He's gone bonkers!' But they did cheer the goal, I give them that, and afterwards I was told they'd cheered the saves I'd made, but this was something that I wouldn't notice. There's not too many crowds like that, though; I don't think even Borough's is one of them.

Going off at half-time I felt great; in the dressing-room, everyone was bubbling. The Boss came up to me, put his arm round my shoulder, and said, 'I'm really proud of you, Ronnie. I knew you wouldn't let me down.' Billy Wallis came up and congratulated me, too, and so did most of the lads. Even old poker face, Jack Noakes, said, 'Done well with those two, didn't he, Ronnie?' It didn't even worry me that in the second half I'd be playing in front of the Kop. In fact when I trotted on for the second half they gave me a cheer, it was fantastic, they applauded me, shouting, 'Well done, the keeper; played, the boy.' Mind you, they followed up with a few other things as well, like, 'We'll put a few past you this half, son,' but that didn't worry me. I was too shy to turn round and answer them; I just stood there not letting on I'd heard them.

Charlie had said to let them come at us for the first ten minutes or so. He said, 'It's a heavy ground, and if they keep carrying the ball, they'll tire. If they whack it into the goalmouth, that's a defender's ball; and Ronnie's picking them like coconuts, aren't you, son? If we're going to score again, we can do it on the break; I've seen milk turn quicker than their defenders.'

And it turned out just like he said. They came at us for about twenty minutes or so, most of it through the middle, but they only got in a couple of real shots. One of them was from Emlyn Hughes, it kept very low from right outside the box, but I was watching for those and although I saw it a bit late through all the players, I got down to it by the post, and held it. Then Toshack got up and headed down a cross for someone to hit, I think it was Evans, and I was lucky with that one, I admit; I just came off my line and hurled myself. The ball hit me and cannoned away, I couldn't tell you where, but when I jumped up again, the lads were patting me on the back and it was in touch, so I suppose someone cleared it. A goalkeeper's got to have a bit of luck, sometimes.

The Kop started singing, 'Borough's going to lose, Borough's going to lose, ee-ay-addey-oh, Borough's going to lose,' to taunt us, I suppose, but as far as I was concerned, it was the other way around. We were still a goal up, and if anybody looked like losing, it was them.

About the middle of the half, we nearly got another; again, it was just like Charlie Macintosh had said. Bob Cullen suddenly got away on the right-wing, he had tremendous acceleration and he loved moving out there. He took the centre-half with him, he cut the ball back across the edge of the box, and Tommy Dougall came in like the wind and hit it. I thought it was there all the way, but Clemence got up and somehow pushed it over the bar; it was a fabulous save. They were shouting at me from the Kop, 'That's the way, son; watch him! That's how you ought to keep goal!'

They got a bit desperate then – which the Boss had also said they would – and they started belting all these high ones into the penalty box, for Toshack – there was no one else likely to get up to them. But by now I'd really got myself dug in, I reckoned any ball up to twelve or fifteen yards out was mine, and I was calling for them, which I'd been too nervous to do, early on. Once I came out and got flattened, and that's a terrible feeling. You're so unprotected when you're up there in the air, and when they hit you, you can only pray that the referee's seen it, that he's got the guts to whistle – especially if it's away from home, and he's got something like the Kop on his back. Anyway, this one did whistle, which was just as well, as they'd knocked the ball into the net while I was down.

When the final whistle went, we were still one up and as I heard it, I jumped into the air, it was the happiest moment of my life. That's what I told a reporter afterwards, and that's what they put on the photograph of me jumping, that

Monday: His Happiest Moment. That was something true in the papers, anyway. Ray McGraw ran up to me and I hugged him, Arthur Prescott put his arm round my neck, even Jack Noakes was grinning all over his face and saying, 'Well done, the keeper!' while on the Kop, I'll give them that, they were applauding; I could hear them shouting, 'Played, young Ronnie! Well done, lad!'

In the dressing-room, everyone was going mad, shaking hands and dancing around, slapping me on the back, hugging me. Charlie Macintosh came rushing in, he put his arms round me and he said, 'Ronnie, you're the best young goalkeeper I've ever seen! the best! I take back what I said about you playing for England at twenty-one! Nineteen! You'll play by the time you're nineteen! I'll put money on that! Who wants to lay me odds?' Then Billy Wallis came up in that quiet way of his and said, 'Proud of you, Ronnie, proud of you,' which meant a lot to me, and finally even the Chairman. He came into the dressing-room with his bowler hat on, shook hands with me, very, very solemn, and said, 'Congratulations, my boy.'

When we came out to get on the coach, there were a lot of Borough fans gathered around it, giving us a cheer, jumping up and down and shouting, 'Good old Ronnie! Great game, Ron!' which chuffed me, and there was more of them on the station platform, too, when we got there. Several of them asked me for an autograph, and I signed a few before Charlie Macintosh chased them away, saying, 'Give the lad a bit of peace!' then he took me into the station buffet and said, 'What'll you have, son? Champagne or a Bovril?' I said, 'A Bovril.' At that time I didn't go much for anything but the odd beer, and I was too excited then to be able to get one down.

On the train, in the restaurant car, the cards come out, and the lads were ordering bottle after bottle. Very happy, everyone was, but no one was as happy as the old hangers-on, the directors' friends; well away, they were, before we were halfway through the meal. One big bloke, he was in television or something, kept raising his glass to me and saying, 'To the new goalkeeper! To the next England goal-keeper!' which was all right at first, but got a bit embarrassing after a time, especially as the other lads started making a bit of a joke of it, asking me whether Gordon Banks knew, and was I going to drop him a line when I was nineteen, so he could just step down quietly?

There were a couple of London reporters on the train, too, one from the *Daily News*, Bert Grey, he was a London boy, the other from the *Courier*, Lew Prentice, a little bloke who'd played a bit himself, once. They both seemed all right, they were both very nice, asking me a lot of questions, though not as many as Doug Green. Arthur Prescott said, 'See that they pay you, Ronnie. Tenner a time, that's worth,' but Bert Grey, who was quite funny, he'd shoot out these remarks in a straight-faced way, said, 'That's all right, Ronnie; we won't charge you, this time.'

When I got home, the old man was dancing around, he was so pleased. There'd been a telegram from him at the ground, another one from Mike: 'Congratulations on the first of many,' very nice. The old man said, 'It's on the box tomorrow, it's on the box, the Big Match!' and that was a very strange feeling, the Sunday afternoon, sitting there after lunch, watching yourself, then them stopping the film and showing it again, and Jimmy Hill there with his beard, saying it was one of the best goalkeeping debuts he could remember. I must say it didn't look too bad, especially that first save, and the one from Toshack, and when they showed the time in the second half, when I just came out and flung myself blind, I felt like I was living it again, I was so tensed up. I was entitled to be, as well, because after it had hit me, the ball looked as if it was going straight to one of their blokes, but Ray McGraw dived in and just got a deflection, and Jackie Noakes banged it into touch.

*

Mike had been round that morning to congratulate me, wheeling his old bike, cycle clips on, as usual. He shook me by the hand and said, 'Ronnie, I'm very, very proud of you,' he was smiling all over his face. 'I've read all the reports, all of them, and you were obviously great. Mind you: I told you, didn't I? Remember when you were so small? Remember when you were afraid you'd never make it? You remember that time, don't you, Mr Blake?' and the old man said yes, he did; he'd never been too sure how to take Mike.

'Well,' said Mike, 'now it's happened. You're there to stay, Ronnie. There for years.' I said, 'I hope so,' and he said, 'Of course you are. What did Charlie say?'

'Charlie?' I said, forgetting old Mike and his names, 'Oh, the Boss. He was very nice. He was very pleased,' and Mike said, 'He's entitled to be,' then the old man said, which I hadn't wanted him to, 'He said Ronnie would be playing for England by the time he's nineteen.'

Mike smiled and said, 'Come down a couple of years then, has he?' obviously remembering, then he said, 'Well, a few more games like that, and he may be right. Gordon Banks can't go on forever.'

Seeing yourself on television that first time; it was strange. It was you, if you see what I mean, and yet it wasn't you. I quite enjoyed it, because I'd played well, but I started thinking what it would be like if I hadn't played well, which was bound to happen, some time, if I'd thrown a couple in. Imagine seeing all that, over and over again, in slow motion.

The other thing about it's harder to explain. Television; it's you and it's not you, if you see what I'm getting at. It's a stranger, and yet it's you, doing the things you can never see yourself doing and, if you're a professional footballer, doing them in front of thousands of people. So it's embarrassing, as well, because it's not that you want to look great, you're just concerned with not looking stupid. Like the shot they showed at one time on the BBC every Saturday night, Match of the Day; Gordon West, the Everton goalkeeper, doing his nut with his defence, giving them a right rollicking – you can tell, although you can't hear a thing – and at the same time rolling chewing gum all round his mouth. How could he feel when he saw that, week after week after week? So maybe I was lucky that the first time it happened to me, I'd had such a good game; but nevertheless, it's still a shock.

Still, that was nothing to what happened after Monday. The first thing was a new contract. When I got to Borough that morning, I was told the Boss wanted to see me. I went up to his office and he flipped this contract across the desk at me and said, 'Here, get your father to sign it.' No wonder he didn't discuss it or anything; it was just fabulous. For a kick-off, it put me on a basic salary of £50 a week. Then on top of that came all the bonuses for position in the League, size of the crowds, and the rest of it, with more if we won anything; the League, the Cup, or any of the European Cups. My head went round, I couldn't believe it, and I wondered what the old man would say who'd been slogging round the pavements all his life for just a few quid a week. In fact funnily, after the first sort of impact, this was what I thought of more than anything; how unfair it was, in a way, like winning the pools, or something.

The Boss slapped me on the back and said, 'It'll start right away; I've back-dated it. This week, you should pick up about seventy-five quid. The club's got a saving scheme if you want to come in on it; I advise all unmarried players on first team contracts to join. Tell your father. See the papers this morning?'

'Yeah,' I said, 'most of them,' which I had. In fact I was still trying to get over those when he sprung this contract on me. Great big photographs. Interviews; what I'd said and what I was supposed to have said. The ones by Bert Grey and Lew Prentice were okay. Headlines about 'New Teenage Goalkeeping Star' and all the rest of it. It was fabulous in one way, but in another, it frightened you; it was like you'd suddenly been put into a big cage, all flood-lit, and thousands and thousands of people were looking in on you, just staring, waiting to see what you did next.

Driving down to Snaresbrook, Billy Wallis said, 'Give you a good contract, did he?'

'Fabulous,' I said, 'fabulous,' and he said, not looking at me, like he often did, 'Don't go mad.'

'I won't,' I said, 'I'm going to save all I can,' and I meant that, because there wasn't much I needed. Bill nodded, like he was pleased, and he said, 'A lot of 'em go mad.'

I knew I wouldn't. To me, the ones that went mad were the ones who were living away from home, who hadn't got any background; or the ones that came from *bad* homes. I knew of some like that; London boys. There'd been one or two during the time I'd been with Borough. They'd shot up, they'd looked like they were going to be good, but when they came into the money, it was too much for them. So I knew what Billy meant; especially with him being a London boy, too.

Down at the ground, they were all waiting for me, taking the mickey. 'How's the new sensation? How's the flying teenager? What's it like to be a star on television? When are you going to write your book, then?' Another of the lads said, 'Wait till he's nineteen! Joe Royle of Everton did one at nineteen!' and someone else said, 'How I Thrilled the Kop; by the Flying Teenager.' I didn't mind.

But from then on, it was like I'd crossed a bridge. The Boss put it well. He said, 'That's your initiation ceremony, Ronnie. That's your baptism of fire. If you can face the Kop, you can face anything. There's two things you never know in football till you've seen them. How a young player will stand up in a League match, and how he'll stand up in an international.'

I got back in the middle of the afternoon, we didn't do that much on Monday, though I liked to keep up with the

94

exercises. I did them with Don Collins, the trainer, he was great on things like that; all the movements, all the gymnastics. He knew what you needed and he knew what you could take, which didn't make him too popular with one or two of the boys, because they couldn't skive with him. He was very big on the stomach muscles and the ground exercises; when I started under him he had me aching all over, but I soon began feeling the benefit. He was a physiotherapist, not like the old kind of trainer that was an ex-pro who sort of picked it up as he went along. I heard a few stories about some of them; how they'd be massaging you for a broken leg, and that. But old Don could blind you with science, he was great on the old metatarsals, the meniscus and all that.

The old man was home; he was on the morning round that week. Sitting in front of the fire with his blue and red post office trousers on, in his braces, reading the *Evening Standard*; there was a bit about me in there, as well.

He said, 'Great Ron, great. They was all on about you down the sorting office. Quite a few on the round, too; ones that know I'm your father.'

Then I showed him the contract. I didn't tell him anything about it, I just showed him, and I watched his face, wondering how he'd take it, feeling proud and yet, at the same time – I don't know – feeling guilty. And the more he read, the more amazed he looked. His eyes got bigger, his mouth started widening; he glanced at me once like he couldn't believe it. Then he said, just looking ahead, in a kind of daze, 'Well, that's amazing. Well, I can hardly believe that, Ron. Well, that's wonderful, that is. Wonderful.'

Then he called my mother in from the kitchen and said, 'Look! Look what they're giving Ron!' and she read it, too, standing there in her apron – you hardly ever saw her when she wasn't in her apron – and she said, 'Marvellous, Ronnie! Isn't that marvellous!' and she put her arm round me and gave me a kiss.

I said, 'You've got to sign it, Dad,' and he shook his head and kept on looking at it, like he was afraid the print would disappear, or something. He was sort of mouthing things to himself, numbers. Now and again I'd make out, 'Forty,' or maybe, 'Twenty,' till at last he asked me, 'How much you reckon this'll be worth to begin with, Ronnie?' I said, 'The Boss said seventy-five quid,' and he shook his head again. He said, 'Seventy-five quid. At seventeen. It don't seem possible, do it?'

'No,' I said, 'it don't.'

'Well,' he said, 'I'm proud of you, Ron. I'm very very glad for you.'

'Not just for me,' I said, 'for all of us,' but he said, 'No, it's yours, Ron, it's only fair. You put it away, son. You look after it. You make hay while the sun shines. You never know your luck. Please God you'll be making it for twenty years, but *you* know; a goalkeeper.'

Mum said, 'Fred!' but I reckoned he was right. I said, 'The Boss says they've got a savings scheme; for players that aren't married,' and Dad said, 'Well, use it. Look after it. You pay your keep here. We don't want no more than your keep.' And I felt very choked; I don't know why. It wasn't how I'd expected to feel. I somehow felt that I was letting them down, though without ever meaning to; that in doing what I'd done, earning what I was going to earn, I was kind of cutting myself off from them.

That Friday, when they paid me, I went into the West End and I bought my mother a new handbag, I bought the old man a raincoat, because I knew he needed it, and I bought my sister a silk scarf.

Most of the time, though, it was still like a bit of a dream. The publicity, the people ringing up from the papers, knowing I'd be in the team again, that Saturday. In a way, I was grateful for the training, because at least it kept your feet on the ground.

That week, we were at home to Leeds United, which was

another hard one. Mick Jones, Allan Clarke, Peter Lorimer with those thirty-yard right-footers, Jack Charlton getting in your way on the goal line. But this time I wasn't so worried, even if it *was* my first home game which, like the Boss said to me, was something I had to get over. He said, 'You'll feel better when it's out of the way. That's one reason I was glad to put you in at Liverpool. It may be a hard one; but at least it's away. This game, though, you come in on the crest of a wave. You'll have the whole crowd behind you.'

To me, that could be good or it could be bad; though obviously it was better than having them against you. But I was pleased I wouldn't have to share a room with Graham Gibbs again and have him going through the whole Leeds team. I could just imagine him; watch out for Mick Jones jumping ten feet in the air, watch out for Allan Clarke's shot, watch out for Billy Bremner coming through. The Boss made one or two good points at the team talk, especially on Clarke. He said, 'He'll go through a game like a sleepwalker; and that's just when he's dangerous. He comes to life when you least expect it. Watch him on the turn. Watch his right foot; there's hardly any backlift. That's how he beats a lot of goalkeepers; he's made the shot before they've set themselves.'

In fact this was something that I found in the first minutes. A cross came over from the left, Jackie Noakes got up and headed it away, it went to the edge of the box, to Clarke, and as soon as I saw that I was moving. It was just as well, because whoof! he'd hit it with his right foot, caught it beautifully. It came in very fast and low, but I was moving to it, and I held it. I got a right old cheer from the crowd behind the goal; it was the South goal, where most of the noise came from, and a lot of the aggro.

When I'd run down there from the other end, where we'd been kicking in, they gave me a great old welcome, and it made me feel good; my first home game, and they were behind me already. And getting off to another early save, made me feel good; my first home game, and they were like I had at Anfield; that was fine, as well.

I noticed like I had at Liverpool how much faster everything seemed to happen, how much pressure they put on you. This Jones was very strong; even stronger than Toshack. Early on, there was a corner that Gray took from the left, an inswinger, and though I went up for it and got it all right, he flattened me, Jones. It was a free kick, but I realized that I couldn't take any chances. The next time a ball like that came over and he challenged me for it, I punched it.

After that, we got on top of them for a spell. We were playing some good stuff in midfield. Tommy Dougall and the other two, Harry and Graham, holding it well and spraying it about, but although we had more of the play, we weren't really making openings.

I don't like it when it gets like that. The more you play as a goalkeeper, the higher up you go, the more you realize that it's dangerous to have too much of the play, unless you're scoring goals. But if you're really hammering the other side, you're hitting the post, you're hitting the bar, you're hitting the keeper's legs, but you're not putting it in; then – watch out. The other side are going to come away, and maybe score. What's more, if you're a goalkeeper, they're liable to catch you cold.

Which is just what happened. There couldn't have been more than a few minutes to half-time when they hit a long one out of defence to Eddie Gray, on the left, and he came away like a tank. Arthur Prescott tried to take him with a slide tackle, but he hopped over his legs, and that gave them the man over. Ray McGraw had to move out of the middle to challenge him, he made to go outside him, then cut it back inside.

Ray bought the dummy, but I didn't; I'd been expecting a centre, even if he'd gone like he'd made to, and beaten

Ray down the wing. Out of the corner of my eye, I'd seen someone coming in fast on my left. There wasn't time to do no more than belt out of goal and go for him and the ball feet first. The ball whacked against my leg and bounced away; when I jumped up again, I saw it had been Mick Jones, and it was out of play. He said, 'Lucky there, lad,' but to me, it wasn't lucky. I'd been practising these feet-first saves for weeks down at Snaresbrook, with the Boss. They were something that had come in from the Continent, according to him, though I'd seen Gordon Banks do them, at the Bridge and on the box. What they did was give you a chance to get balls you'd be that fraction late on, if you dive at them.

The Boss was really pleased with me about it, at half-time. 'That was a great save,' he said, 'a great save. You see what I told you? You see how it works?' Then he rollicked the defence for letting it happen, and he rollicked the attack for hitting too many high crosses. He said, 'You can kill them on the ground. You can murder Jackie Charlton on the ground. Play to feet. Give it to Bob on the floor; he can play it off or he can turn and take the big fellow on.'

But we were still a very young team, and it wasn't so easy. Leeds had all the experience, they were really well organized. We'd play it off the cuff, so to speak, where they could do a thing by heart. The Boss had had a lot to say about the way they used free kicks, all kinds of dead ball situations, with Jackie Charlton coming upfield. Funnily enough, they only had a couple of corners in the first half, and he didn't come up for them, but when they got one early in the second half, he did. He plonked himself right on the goal line, bang in front of me, this great, big fellow, so I had not a hope of getting round him to the ball.

The Boss had said, 'If he does that, just go right through him. Take him, the ball and everything; no referee will ever penalize you and, if you bounce off him, then you'll get a foul; especially at home.' But looking at him now, how big he was, it was lot easier said than done; it would be like knocking over a telegraph pole.

Arthur Prescott had a go at him, he said, 'Why don't you move, you big so-and-so?' but Charlton said, 'I'm allowed to stand here; you ask the ref.' But when the ball came over, an inswinger, it was too far out of the goal for him to get at, and it wouldn't have been my ball, anyway. Ray McGraw got up to it and headed it out, and that was that, for the moment.

But they were always doing something, Leeds, always putting you under pressure. Tommy Dougall hadn't any time for them. He'd said, 'They're a dead ball team, that's all, a free kick team. When they score a goal from a fluid situation, they open a bottle of champagne in the dressing-room.' To Tommy, this wasn't football, just as anyone who couldn't keep the ball in the air for five minutes on end or balance it on his head wasn't a footballer.

In fact they were diabolical, these free kicks from Giles. It didn't matter whether he took them from the left or from the right, with one foot or the other, they always did just what he wanted them to do, they were always perfectly placed, just curling out of your reach as you went for them, on to somebody's head. And it was amazing how Jackie Charlton could sneak in on the blind side, big as he was, and get his head to the ball when no one expected it.

It happened once when Giles took a free kick from over on the left; everybody was looking for Clarke and Jones, but Charlton suddenly came running in from the wing and got his head to it. I jumped for it, I reckoned I'd have got it if it had been lower, but as it was, it went over the bar; I didn't have to look, the crowd went, 'Oo-oo-ooh.' In the Reserves, I'd really have told the defence, but in the first team, I hadn't got the confidence yet. I said to Jackie Noakes, 'Somebody should have gone with him,' and Jackie got on at Bob Cullen for not coming back with Jackie Charlton, waving his arms and shouting.

Next, it was Lorimer. Someone gave him a square pass about thirty-five yards out, there didn't seem to be any danger, but I was wary of him, after being told. Joe Lyons was backing in front of him, it looked as if what he'd probably do was give the ball inside, instead of which he suddenly pushed it forward and shot. Joe was partly blocking my view, and I only saw it late. I got my body behind it all right, but I wasn't well set to hold it; it hit me a terrific thump on the chest and bounced away. When that happens, you're helpless, you can only hope one of your team will get it away, or someone will hit the rebound where you can reach it. Besides, Mick Jones is always following up on anything like that, and he did this time, he was in like a flash, but thank goodness he couldn't quite catch hold of it, the ball was about knee height. He volleyed it with the inside of his foot, but I sprang up and got my fingers to it, and just managed to knock it over the bar. It must have looked like a great save, but this time I admit I was lucky.

So there it was; a draw, no goals by either side, and naturally I was delighted when the whistle went, not having given away a goal in my first two matches. In the dressing-room the Boss said, 'I told you about Lorimer.' I said, 'I know, Boss, I was unsighted,' and he turned to Billy Wallis, he said, 'Did you hear that, wee Billy? Unsighted! He's learning quickly, isn't he?' But he told me I'd done well, he was happy with me. He said, 'A point against Leeds isn't bad, even at home.'

This time, the old man had been there, with my mother and sister, too. When I got home he was so happy, he could hardly talk. He said, 'Well, Ron, you were marvellous, wasn't he, dear? Your mother and I ... well, we could hardly believe it. Sitting there. Watching you pull off all them saves, against the greatest in the land. Well, it was just amazing.'

Mum said, 'You should have seen the look on his face;

walking on air, he was. Especially when you made those two saves, one after the other. My heart came into my mouth, I can tell you!'

'Mine did and all,' I said.

'And they're all so pleased about you,' Mum said, 'all the season ticket holders and people sitting round us. They all said you were the best young goalkeeper they'd seen for years. And in the end, Dad couldn't hold it back any longer. He said, "He's my son!" And they were all congratulating him, saying how proud he must be, how one day you were sure to play for England.'

'Well,' I said, 'there's a long way to go before that.'

'I don't know,' the old man said. 'He said so, didn't he? Charlie Macintosh said so.'

We celebrated that night, I took them all out to dinner at a posh restaurant in Notting Hill Gate. Many's the time I'd passed that place and looked in the window, wondering what it must be like, and I suppose I could have afforded it before, but somehow, I couldn't bring myself to go in, even when I wanted to impress a bird. I suppose I thought in a way that I didn't belong there. But now, on the new contract, I told myself I belonged there as much as anybody else, maybe more than quite a lot of them. And I was always hearing the other lads go on about where *they'd* been, the clubs in the West End, the restaurants in Soho and the King's Road, and all. So this was where I chose, and not just for me, for all of us, the whole family, maybe because I wanted someone with me, but also because I was saying; here we are: the lot of us. We can afford it.

The old man wasn't that keen at first. He had this thing about knowing his place, not going where he didn't think he'd be wanted, but Mum was very excited about it, I knew, even though she didn't like to go against him. He was sort of wriggling about and saying, 'No, Ronnie, maybe another time; I can't go like I am now, can I?' and I told him, 'Put on your blue suit, then, there's nothing wrong with your suit. And wear that coat I gave you. This is your chance.'

In the end I managed to persuade him, and we went. Not only that, it was a fabulous evening. It was an Italian place, very low lighting, pictures of gondolas and things all over the walls, table lamps made out of bottles; the old man sat down and looked around like he was afraid something was going to jump out of the wall at him. They brought us these menus, four great big cards the size of a newspaper, and Dad said, 'What's this? I don't understand none of it.'

Mum said, 'It's written in English underneath,' but he said, 'I still don't understand it. I don't even know what they are in English.' Most of them were new to me, as well, but I didn't let on, I didn't want to encourage him. When the waiter came up I said, 'What's good today?' and he told us this and that. Then another waiter came over and pulled him aside, whispering something to him, and he turned back to me and said, 'You are the Borough goal-keeper!'

I said, 'Yes, that's right,' I was chuffed, it was the first time this kind of thing had happened to me. Later on I was going to get sick of it, but this time it was nice, especially as they all came buzzing round us then and made a big fuss of us. Mum loved it, and even the old man perked up and relaxed. They sent a bottle of wine over to us, the head waiter came up, the proprietor, everybody; they had me signing the menu, signing cards for them, and they kept telling me to come in again. They were all football fans, though mostly of Italian teams I'd barely heard of. I wasn't used to wine, but we all drank a bit, and in the end every-one was toasting me, saying how they hoped I'd never let in a goal, and maybe it worked, because I didn't, for the next two matches.

We went to Blackpool, and we got another 0–0 draw there, then we won at home to Burnley, 2–0. Mind you, I had a bit of luck in both games. In the Blackpool match Tony Green hit the bar, and against Burnley, Arthur Prescott and Joe Lyons both kicked off the line. It's a marvellous feeling for a goalkeeper, that; when he's beaten, he's down on the deck, and he's waiting to hear the crowd shout for a goal, then someone comes to the rescue; like the kiss of life.

The papers started writing me up, then; RONNIE THE KID IS STILL UNBEATEN, all that sort of tripe! Hardly a day went by when I hadn't got some reporter asking me questions. The lads helped me sort them out, they'd say, 'This one's a right nice fellow, you can talk to him,' or, 'Watch what you say to that bloke; he'll drop you in it.' To me, the worst questions were the ones on the telly, because you knew that whatever you said was going to go out on the box; in other words if you made a Charlie of yourself, you did it in front of millions of people.

It happened to me after the Burnley game; a message came down to the dressing-room, would I go back on the pitch when I was changed and do an interview with Rupert Vincent. I shook my head, I said, 'No, not me, what do I want to do that for? No thanks,' but the other lads all said, 'Don't be silly, there's fifteen quid in it. All you've got to say is "Yes, Rupert, thanks, Rupert, that's right, Rupert." He won't ask you nothing complicated; he just smiles at the camera and waits for you to stop talking.'

So I went out again through the tunnel. The floodlights were off now and it was all dark and very gloomy, except for the lights the T V people had, in the middle of the pitch, where they'd put the camera. I felt funny coming out into an empty stadium, where before there'd been more than forty-five thousand people, all shouting their heads off. It had been a heavy old pitch that day, after some rain – it always tends to churn up, at Borough – and I could have done without slipping and sliding across the mud in the new boots I'd bought; black, soft leather.

Rupert Vincent was standing there with a mike in his

hand; he gave me a big smile and said, 'Hallo, Ronnie!' like we'd known each other for years, though I'd never met him before. Then he talked to the bloke behind the camera and he talked to the bloke on the lights, was it all right, where should we both stand, and finally he turned back to me and said, 'Well, how does it feel to be a First Division star at the age of seventeen, Ronnie?'

What do you say to a question like that? I just sort of stared at him, I felt like someone had hit me on the head. In the end, I said, 'It feels all right,' and he gave this laugh of his and said, 'I bet it does, Ronnie; a few weeks ago, if someone had come up to you and told you you were going to get in the Borough first team and not let through a goal in four matches, would you have believed them?'

'No,' I said, 'I wouldn't.' What was I meant to say? Then he asked how did I feel when those two shots were kicked off the line; I said, 'Very, very relieved,' and did I think they were going to be goals; I said, 'Yes.' Then he mentioned something that the Boss was meant to have said about me, that I had the perfect temperament for a goal-keeper, did I agree? and I said, 'I don't know.' I'd have looked a right burke saying, 'Yes.'

When I got back to the dressing-room I was sweating, although it was so cold out there. Tommy Dougall looked at me and he said, 'How does it *feel*?' I said, 'Come off it. I've had enough of that from *him*.'

He said, 'Did he make you feel like a performing dog? Going through his tricks? Standing on his hind legs for a biscuit?'

I said, 'He did a bit, yeah.'

Tommy said, 'One of these days, I'm going to go out there and ask him how *he* feels. Asking stupid questions, Grinning into the camera like a film star. Never mind, Ronnie, you'll get your biscuit. You'll get your fifteen quid.'

'Yeah,' I said. 'Well, I can tell you one person who won't be looking at the box tonight.'

Harry Jackson said, 'Get out! As soon as it comes on, you won't be able to take your eyes off it.'

And in fact I did see it, simply through being with the family, and them getting so excited. I was meant to be going out with a bird, but when I got home, they were full of it, they'd just heard it was going to be Borough and Burnley, and I couldn't disappoint them, especially now I knew I'd be on it myself, however big a burke I looked. Mum said, 'Ring her up, tell her to come round and watch it, too,' but I didn't want that, it's embarrassing, bringing a bird home, so I just rang up and said I was sorry, I'd been injured. That's one thing about being a goalkeeper, when there's something you don't want to do on a Saturday night; although in fact this was something I *did* want to do. But I certainly didn't tell her I was on the box.

I was a bit more used to it now, seeing myself; I didn't keep thinking, is that me? So *that*'s what I look like! Big, dark, surly-looking fellow. In fact I began to realize it could be useful, especially with the two shots that beat me, because I could see what I did wrong. The first one I didn't think I had much chance with. This big Steve Kindon went down the left-wing, got to the line, and pulled it back for Fletcher to hit. But the second time, late in the game, when Dave Thomas nearly scored, I reckoned I should have been off my line a bit quicker; I was too long making up my mind that he wasn't going to centre.

Then came the interview, and honestly, it was terrible. The worst thing was that the family sat there lapping up every word; the old man, he looked like he'd just opened his Christmas stocking. But to me, there was this gormless nit there, answering the questions like he couldn't even understand them, let alone think of anything to say. And if I felt like this, knowing what had happened, knowing all the problems, then what would anybody else feel?

When it was over, Dad turned to me and said, 'Well, I think you done well, son. They weren't easy questions, those. Say the wrong thing, and they'd all be jumping on you. They'd all be calling you big-headed,' which was one way of looking at it. I felt a bit better, then. My sister said she thought Rupert Vincent was ever so good-looking, which was like her, and Mum asked me was I nervous. I said, 'Yes, I was. I was very nervous,' but she said I didn't look it, which amazed me, because to me I looked like I was terrified.

I mentioned it to Billy Wallis, driving down to Snaresbrook that Monday; you could talk to Bill, and he said, 'Well, the game's changed, hasn't it? Television and all. There wasn't much of that in my day. Now, it's like show business. You just got to put up with it. I reckon it's all right, if they pay you.'

It was all happening, I can tell you; I didn't really know what had hit me. This newspaper wanting that, this magazine wanting the other. Sometimes they paid me, sometimes they didn't, but the lads were helpful, they'd tell me what to ask for. Only I couldn't ask for it off my own bat, I was too shy; I could only say, like if they asked me, how much, 'Twenty-five quid,' or whatever the boys had told me to say; mumbling it, and hoping that they wouldn't start arguing. But they never did, thank heaven.

That week, I went in with Harry Jackson to a shop in the Charing Cross Road that was owned by a mate of his and I bought myself a sheepskin coat. The bloke was very good, he knocked ten quid off it, but it still cost me forty-five. I'd never paid anything like that for a coat in my life, but five or six of the lads had them, and Harry said it was a bargain. Arthur Prescott said, 'Don't listen to him, Ron, he's getting a commission,' but he'd got one of them himself.

So I put it on; I felt great in it. It was so warm, and it looked so good. The bloke was a Borough fan, he said, 'Pity you can't wear it in the goalmouth.' I said, 'It is, and all,' thinking of the rainy days, especially when there wasn't much to do, when you walked up and down in the mud and your feet got cold and your fingers started to go numb. I ran my fingers down the front of it. It felt all rich and thick, and I suddenly thought of the old man, out in his postman's coat in all kinds of weather.

It was amazing, what we got given by the fans, the hangers-on. The meals, the clothes, the entertainment. Like one night we were all of us up at the Hilton, in Park Lane, to a boxing tournament. Not only that, we were wearing evening dress, and all.

To me, the Hilton was like a foreign country, a place you saw – that you couldn't help seeing, being a skyscraper – yet you never thought you'd get to. But there I was; coming in across the entrance lobby, wearing my sheepskin coat, among all these men smoking big cigars, these fabulous looking birds in fur coats and jewellery. I'd hired the dinner jacket, I'd gone along to Moss Bros, but the lads had said I ought to buy my own, I ought to have one made, it'd be cheaper in the long run, and there was a tailor who was a Borough fan who'd make it cheap. It seemed to me at times that everybody was a Borough fan.

The boxing thing was strange. We all sat there and had a right old nosh, the blokes in their dinner jackets, the birds all done up to the nines, and in the middle of the room there was this boxing ring. Somebody got up and said, 'We're pleased and proud to have here with us tonight as our guests the Borough United football team,' and we all got up while they applauded, then a couple of fellows got into the ring and started knocking one another about. To me, boxing had been like down at Lime Grove Baths now and then, for a giggle. But this was funny; it somehow didn't seem to belong – any more than we did.

At home, I was feeling it a bit, I admit it. It was like living in two worlds. Most of the lads didn't have this. Either they were married and they had their own homes, over Southgate or Wood Green or somewhere, or they were from the provinces and lived in digs. There were one or two London boys like Arthur, but by and large, they weren't in the same boat as I was.

Mum helped me fix my black tie that night before I went out, I could never have done it. She said to my Dad, 'He looks wonderful, doesn't he?' but to me, all I looked was out of place, I just couldn't wait to get through the front door. At the Hilton, I was uncomfortable in another way, but I must say none of the lads seemed to feel it, they were all chatting and laughing away, not drinking too much because the Boss was there as well – he caught my eye once and said, 'Not bad, eh? Better than lining up at a soup kitchen in Glasgow!' So I reckoned that in time, maybe I'd get used to it like they had.

At Old Trafford, in my fifth match, I let through my first goal. Georgie Best got it, so I couldn't really complain, and it was a fabulous one, too. It never looked on when he got the ball; it was a high one, he was right in the middle of the box, two or three of our defenders round him, and he brought it down dead cool back to the goal, and before I knew what was happening, he'd spun right round and hit it with his left. I never even saw it. I just stretched out a hand as it whistled past me. You can't make rules for that fellow; what a goal!

Of course it had to happen down the Stretford End where all the aggro was, and they were always doing goalkeepers. They let me have it properly, then, I can tell you, especially when I wouldn't go and pick it out of the net; nothing would have made me; it was like they'd been done out of their prey. 'Go and fetch the so-and-so ball, you so-and-so! What's the matter with you, are you paralysed?' and then, when Arthur went to get it, 'He don't believe it's a goal!' When the game restarted, they borrowed the Kop chant, they started singing, 'Ron's let in a goal, Ron's let in a goal, ee-ay-addey-oh, Ron's let in a goal!' Then the coins started. I heard something whizz into the mud in front of me; I looked down and there it was. A two new pence. I picked it up and ran my finger over it; somebody had filed the edge. I thought, that's nice.

One of them behind the goal yelled out, 'Going to the ref, you pansy? Go on, he can't take it! He's going to tell the ref!' and more of them showered down; one even hit me in the back, though not too hard. Fortunately play was up the other end just then, so I was able to walk as far as the penalty spot, where they couldn't reach me. But it wasn't too nice to think that when it did come up my end again I not only had to stop the ball. I had to think about the coins. I'd heard they threw worse there, too.

In the end, it was Jackie Noakes who told the ref. He came back into the penalty area when United hit a long ball from defence, saw these coins lying around and said, 'They been throwing them at you, then?' I said, 'Yes,' and between us we started picking them up, while Jackie called the ref over. Between us we must have picked up about a dozen. The ref called over a policeman, the copper talked to an inspector, then both of them went over to talk to the Stretford End – who by this time were calling me every name in the book. Then the game got going again, and they kept it just to insults, which wasn't too nice, but at least they couldn't hurt you. They've got some right animals up there.

The end of it was, we lost by that goal. I didn't think I had too bad a match, in fact though we were under quite a bit of pressure there weren't that many saves to make, our defence covered so well. United had a Cup-tie the Saturday after, so maybe they were trying to keep out of trouble, while we'd been knocked out right away by Derby County; we'd got nothing really left to play for.

So it went on till the end of the season. I kept my place, we lost a few, we won a few. But with the Boss there, giving me confidence, I'd got no worries. You don't have, not at seventeen.

Chapter 3

I'd still see Mike around. Very occasionally up the playground, when I went there. There wasn't too much time in the season, and in the summer I'd watch but I wouldn't play. They'd say, 'Go on, Ron, go in goal,' especially the younger kids that had come up since my day, and Mike would say, 'Come on, Ronnie, let's see if you've improved, son,' and now and again I'd go in for a few minutes. Not often, though. It's not that I was big-headed or anything; only that when you're full professional, when you're playing in the League, your attitude changes. You don't want to take risks especially if you're a goalkeeper, because you know on a Saturday you've *got* to take risks. This was something that was hard to explain to them, but I know Mike saw it a bit; if I just watched and wouldn't play, he accepted it, though he'd say something like, 'Got his new gear on today, haven't you, Ronnie? Don't want to spoil *that*.'

About a couple of weeks into the new season, we had a London derby, home to Arsenal. One evening the doorbell went, and it was Mike. He looked a bit embarrassed, staring at the ground and that, but in the end he said, 'I don't like asking you, Ron, but if you *have* got a couple of tickets. A couple of complimentaries. I mean I'll pay; I'll *pay*. They don't have to be complimentaries. It's only that the last Borough–Arsenal match, they closed the gates. I was locked out. Otherwise of course I'd go on the terraces like I normally do.' Then he give this smile at me and said, 'Behind your goal, Ronnie.'

He'd never asked a favour of me before. I felt more embarrassed than he did. I said, 'Yes, Mike, okay, Mike,'

111

though in fact I only got three complimentaries a week, and these always went to the family; but I couldn't take his money. 'All right, Ron,' he said, still looking away from me, 'thanks,' and he went off right away, he never stayed for a chat. I watched him go; walking the old bicycle, of course; not riding.

That summer, we'd been to Scandinavia on tour, a couple of matches in Sweden, a few in Denmark. It had been fabulous. All very relaxed, marvellous weather, great places, fantastic looking girls. We drew a couple of the matches and won the others; none of them were too hard, but to tell the truth, we weren't killing ourselves. The Boss kept saying, 'Go out and enjoy yourselves; go out and play football.' He was in tremendous form, really one of the boys, joking a lot, singing with us, I'd never seen him so relaxed. And there was a very good spirit in the team then, all of us young, all of us mucking in together.

By this time Terry Morgan was fit again and came on the tour, but there wasn't any feeling between us; I was helping him in training, he was helping me. As far as I was concerned, I'd be in as long as I played well, the Boss had told me so, and you couldn't ask more than that.

In Copenhagen, we went to the Tivoli Gardens and we had a right old time, dancing with the birds, going round all the sideshows. The big joke was getting Billy Wallis on one of those big dipper things, he was terrified of them. The Boss offered him five quid if he could stay on for two gos, one after the other, so a couple of us got on with him, and I never saw anyone so nervous as Billy was, before the thing started. When it did, when it started whirling round, and I must say it went at quite a lick, he kept saying, 'I'm going to be sick, I'm going to be sick,' till finally, when it stopped, he said, 'I'm getting out of here!'

But we wouldn't let him out, we'd planned it with the Boss. He struggled like mad, you'd never think he was so strong, a little fellow, but in the end the wheel started again, and I felt a bit sorry for him, he looked terrible. At the end, when we came down the second time, he'd gone limp, like a sack; I was quite worried for a moment. Then he sighed and he shook his head and we helped him out of the car. The Boss came up to him and said, 'Marvellous, Billy; here's your money! Why don't you go and buy a nice ham sandwich with it?'

Poor old Billy, he made a terrible face, I thought he was going to throw up, then he went belting off, and we didn't see him again till the next morning. We were all just falling about. The Boss said, 'He'll be the death of me one day, Billy.' He was always pulling Bill's leg.

Danny was on the tour, and he played terrific. He'd never had a game in the first team before, but you'd never have thought that, the way he took to it. Mind you it wasn't quite as hard there, being friendly games, and the tackling wasn't as tough. The grounds suited him, too, very dry, with the ball always light; he loved a ball like that, Danny. But he still fitted in beautifully. He was doing what he liked at times, taking on two or three at a time, nutmegging them, back-heeling, all the tricks; but making them come off, using them to set up goals.

One he got in Copenhagen was fantastic, the sort of thing I'd seen Pelé score on the television. Someone hit a high cross into the box, and Danny caught it on his instep, flicked it up in the air, then put it in over his head with a bicycle kick. The Boss said in the dressing-room afterwards. 'There he is lads. The White Pelé,' which from then on was what we called him.

Personally, I couldn't wait for the new season. It was a strange thing being at home with so much time on my hands, and yet with plenty of money. Uncomfortable, really, having the old man get up each morning, off on the round, while I stayed in bed, nothing to do all day except enjoy myself. One of the things I did was having driving lessons. All the lads, the first team ones, had a car, and I needed one really, going down every day to Snaresbrook. Besides, Graham knew a dealer who'd knock a bit off if I bought one; another Borough fan – naturally.

That was something to do. Birds were another, naturally. It was nice in the summer, not having to bother about early nights and that; the one consolation, really. The other thing was that naturally, over these last couple of years, I'd got rather out of touch with the blokes round where I lived. The ones you went about with were obviously the ones you played football with. Another thing was the money. I mean, to me it didn't matter, what a bloke earned was his own business, but most of the lads I'd grown up with were still just in ordinary jobs; they were lucky if they were knocking up twenty quid a week. So, like, if we went into a pub, which I did now and again, it was all a bit embarrassing. I'd maybe buy a round, pints and shorts for everybody, and when it came to someone else's turn, he'd feel obliged to do the same, and I knew he couldn't afford it. So I'd be in the position that everybody was obviously expecting me to stand the first round, and I'd want to stand the first round, but at the same time I knew that if I did, I'd be putting the others on the spot.

That was one thing, and the other was the old blokes sitting around the public bar, blokes my father's age and a bit older, in their caps and white shirts without a collar, probably hadn't shaved, they'd maybe been working all their lives to end up earning in a year what I'd make in a couple of months. I knew it wasn't fair, though it wasn't *my* fault, but the atmosphere wasn't nice, you could feel it. Nobody ever come out with anything but it hung in the air; the looks, the sort of things they were saying under their breath.

The trouble was, and this was another reason why I wanted a car, that most of the lads in the team, and the Reserves as well, lived over North London, which was a long way if you went by public transport. The first time I took the driving test I failed, it was ridiculous, really. To me, I'd driven perfectly all right, but the examiner was on about the driving mirror and not stopping long enough at an intersection, so that was that. When I took it again, out at Ealing, I passed, and the next day I went off with Graham to see this geezer, and put down the deposit on a Triumph, a lovely little green sports car.

All the lads were very keen on cars. A couple of them had Jaguars, like Tommy Dougall; he'd made a few quid when he was transferred from Stirling Albion, a couple of seasons before. Graham himself had a red M.G. that he drove at a tremendous lick, but we used to tell him that now he was engaged, now he was settling down, he didn't need it any more. She was a good-looking girl his fiancée, Kathy, but she certainly kept an eye on him. Anyway, it was better now, with the car; I could drive over to North London and I could see my mates.

The first day I brought it to the flats, all the little kids that lived there came crowding round, wanting to touch it, wanting to sit on the bonnet, asking for a ride. One of them said, 'Peter Bonetti's got a bigger one,' they were all Chelsea or Rangers fans. I said, 'Peter Bonetti's been going longer.' Then I went in and brought Mum out. When she saw it she clapped her hands together like she couldn't believe it. I said, 'Get in; I'll give you a ride,' and we drove out, down to Shepherd's Bush, round the White City, up Westway, where I could really let her go. She was laughing and enjoying it like she was a young girl. I said, 'Any time, Mum. Whenever you want a run! Whenever you want to meet your boy friends!' and she laughed and laughed.

When my sister got back from school, I gave her a ride, as well. As for the old man, I didn't quite know how he'd take it. I'd never known him ride anything bigger than a bike, though I believe he'd had a motorcycle now and again, before he was married. He looked at it for a few moments without saying anything, he shook his head once or twice, then in the end he said, 'Well, I'm very proud of you Ron, I'm proud of you.'

Him I drove right out of London, I didn't really know where I was going, down to the river, along the Embankment, till in the end we wound up at a pub in Chiswick where you could sit out in a garden with your drinks. I said, 'Look, Dad, why don't *you* take a few driving lessons, I'll stand you them, then you can use the car whenever you like, seriously, I mean it,' but he said, 'What, me drive one of them? No thanks, Ron. Drove a Royal Mail van a few times. Drove a few trucks in the war, but that's enough for me. I wouldn't feel safe in one of them things.' In a way, I admit, I was a bit relieved, but at least I'd offered it him.

About a week after I'd got it, I was stopped at the lights in the Portobello Road when a cyclist rode up beside me, stuck his head in through the window and said, 'Want to mind how you go in that, Ronnie!' I looked round, and it was old Mike, he was actually riding his bike for once. I said, 'Oh, hello, Mike.' In a way I was a bit relieved, him coming across my car the first time like this, making a joke of it, because now and then I'd wondered how he'd take it; I knew that I was bound to see him. But he seemed to sort of accept it, like it was part of a footballer's life, the way having a pair of boots was. I did offer him a ride in it now and then, but he'd always just smile and shake his head, he'd say, 'No thanks, Ronnie. Feel safer on the old bike.'

Then the season began, and we made a fabulous start. It couldn't have looked much harder, on the face of it; away to Manchester City. I hadn't played against them yet, but I knew all about them, with Frannie Lee buzzing around and Colin Bell coming in from the back, when you least expected him. There was Mike Summerbee, as well; I knew he could hit a ball.

When the team sheet went up, Danny was on it. He was in instead of Ernie Leech. I'd pretty well expected it, I think he had, but we were both chuffed about it. The Boss told us, 'They're made for us, at Maine Road. Playing at home, they'll have to come out at us, and we'll get the space to tear them apart. That centre-forward; when he jumps for the ball, you couldnae get the *Evening News* under his feet, and the whole back four need a couple of tugs to get them around.' He was good like that, the Boss. He'd let you know what to look out for, but at the same time, he could give you confidence.

We needed it and all, after what happened in the first five minutes. City came at us like madmen. Right from the kick-off, we lost possession, Frannie Lee went out to the left, took on a couple of our defenders and crossed, and Colin Bell come galloping in from the right, the blind side, like I'd been warned he would, and hit it whoof! on the volley. Even though I had an idea it'd be on, I hardly had time to get across to it; I reached it with one hand and it went round the left-hand post. Then, at the corner, one of the defenders, Tommy Booth I think it was, got up above our defence and headed it on for Bell, again. This time he headed down and across me, but Arthur kicked it out, by the post.

It was good to make the early save, but still it didn't look too clever for us, the way they were moving the ball, the way they were making openings. Then suddenly Tommy Dougall got away on one of his runs. He was a fantastic ball player, but the trouble was, like the Boss told him, that he was always running into trouble. He once said to Tommy, 'If you went up as many blind alleys in your car as you do on the field Tom, you'd do better on the bus.'

This time, though, he went beautiful. He sent one of them the wrong way, carried on left, like he was going to hit it on the turn, taking the defence with him, then suddenly gave a marvellous reverse pass to Danny, who was running with him. Danny hit it first time with his right foot; it must have been from about twenty-five yards and it just flew in. I hardly even saw it myself before it was in the net, and I know Joe Corrigan didn't. He just stood there like he couldn't believe it, then he looked at his defence and shrugged his shoulders, like to say, 'What could anybody do?' Danny was leaping about like a kangaroo, and I just couldn't stop myself, I had to go running down the field to congratulate him, so there we all were, four or five of us, hugging him, jumping up and down, till I heard one of the City players say, 'You'd think it was the first goal they'd ever scored,' and one of *our* lads said, 'Wait until you see the second!'

Blow me if in a couple of minutes we had *got* a second, and it was Danny again; or rather, though he didn't get it, it was all his. Bob Cullen went out to the right-wing, the way he liked to, took on one of their stoppers, beat him for speed, and crossed very fast. It came to Danny at about knee height. He killed it with the inside of his foot, and I thought we were going to see one of those scissor kicks. Instead, he flicked it again, before it dropped and Jesse Maude came belting in from the left and volleyed it past Corrigan. What a goal! I was really jumping about again, I can tell you.

After that, the game changed a lot, like it often does when one team's been attacking and the other suddenly comes away and gets a goal or two. The first one starts to get worried, all at once they've got to think about saving the game, instead of winning it; the other team, the one that scored, gets its tails up – like we did. Danny and Tommy really started enjoying themselves, it was a treat to see them. Of course they were both individualists, they both liked running the show, but in this match it worked, because playing on the breakaway, you rely on a player who can hold the ball and take a few men on till you get someone up to help him, and if you've got two who can do it, all the better.

Watching Danny, it was amazing to think he was playing

in his first League Match. He got clobbered a couple of times, the second one he was brought down very hard from behind and I got a bit worried about him, he was rubbing his knee, but Dan Collins come on and soon had him right. In the dressing-room at half-time he was full of it; we all were. The Boss said, 'We've got 'em now. Just keep doing what you're doing; and hold on very tight these first five minutes. If you let 'em get a quick goal, they might come back into it again.'

In fact they nearly did. Tommy started off on one of his dribbles, he was maybe getting a bit cocky, he lost the ball, and City came away; Bell to Lee, out on the left, a return pass, he jumped over it, Summerbee hit it, and I had to make a reflex save, I just reached up for it, I hadn't got much idea about it, but luckily it went over the top. We cleared the corner all right, and from then on, we got control again. They did score right at the finish, when Frannie Lee took one across the edge of the box and hit it on the turn with his left, right into the top corner, but by then it didn't matter. We'd been well worth it.

Wednesday we were at home to Everton, another hard one, especially as we knew that this time we'd have to make the running, being the home team. Danny kept his place, which wasn't surprising after all the publicity he'd got; TEENAGE WONDER BOY SINKS CITY and all the rest of it. They'd interviewed him on the television, too, and he'd come out well. My sister liked him, and all, she said, 'Oo, isn't he nice,' which I'd never heard her say when I was on. Danny wasn't like me, he lapped it all up, though he didn't say that much when they interviewed him. As for me, I was pleased, not only pleased for him but for me as well, because now they'd got somebody else to write about, someone even younger than I was and a forward at that, someone that scored goals. A goalkeeper is nothing like as glamorous as a forward.

The Everton game started well. We played some lovely

football in the first twenty minutes; we'd have had one or two if Gordon West hadn't made some good saves, and the only shot they had was just a long one from Colin Harvey that I didn't have any trouble with; well placed, up in the right-hand corner, but I had a lot of time to see it.

Then we scored. Danny was in it, again. Graham hit one of his long balls from midfield, which he always did very well. Danny had the centre-half up his back, but he laid it off, right to Tommy Dougall, coming in, and immediately ran away left for the return ball. Naturally the defence went with him, but when he reached it, he did a lovely turn, the sort of thing you see George Best do, and laid it back across the goal for Bob Cullen to smack it past Westy.

Alan Ball started buzzing again, he had fantastic energy, and he did everything so quick you had to be right on your toes whenever he was in possession, or likely to have it. You could hear that piping high voice of his telling the others what to do, calling for the ball, telling them off, he really ran the show. Once he got in a shot from a cross by Jackie Husband; there wasn't a lot of power behind it because he didn't have much chance to set himself, but he hit it quickly – which actually is most important of all, the thing that really worries a keeper most. I think if it had been a bit faster, it would have scored, but as it was, I managed to get down to it.

Early in the second half, we got another goal. Harry Jackson, who was having a terrific game in midfield, using it beautifully, square balls and one-twos and that, sent Jesse Maude away. Jesse went down the right, he got in a lovely cross under pressure, and Danny went up above the defence and headed it across goal. Bob Cullen came in from the blind side and hit it on the half volley. It went like a bomb, and I don't know how Westy stopped it, it must have been an instinctive save. All he could do, anyway, was just block it, and Tommy Dougall put it in. So we won that one, too.

The next was the match that really meant something to me, though. In a way, I suppose it was the one I'd been waiting for, ever since I signed for Borough. You can guess which it was: Chelsea, away.

All the rest of that week, I had this expectation building up in me. I'd played at Stamford Bridge often enough of course, in the Reserves and in the juniors. I remember the first time, which was an experience in itself, although there was hardly anyone there; a Southern Youth Cup match or something. But all it was then was just a great feeling, I'd done it, I was playing on the Bridge and naturally I was glad to do well – which I did. But now it was the whole works; London derby, a great big crowd, the lot; and Peter Bonetti in the other goal. Everyone I knew there, watching. People I'd grown up with. I just had to do well, I just couldn't let myself down. It wasn't like Liverpool that first time, nor the first home game. This time I knew I *could* do it. The question was, would I?

All that week, before the game, the kids in the flats had been taking the mickey out of me, telling me, 'Let a few through, Ron,' or, 'Ossie'll put a couple past you Saturday, Ron.' One of them even put a couple of Chelsea stickers on the back window of my car.

In the bus, going to the game, Danny and a few others, in the back of the coach, were singing, some others had a card school going, but I sat on my own, just looking out of the window. The Boss noticed, he asked me, 'Not worried, are you, Ronnie? This is one ground we always do well.'

I said, 'I know, Boss. I'll be okay.' He patted me on the shoulder and said, 'You'll do *me*.' Naturally I didn't tell him what was going through my mind.

It was a lovely sunny day, and there must have been sixty thousand there. We heard in the dressing-room they'd closed the gates. I put my cap on, I reckoned I'd be needing it. Running out, the pitch was great, all springy and lush, like it is at the start of the season. There'd been a bit of aggro in the Shed, behind the goal where we were shooting in. The coppers were heaving a few of them away and there was a right old struggle with one of them, a Borough fan, it took four of them. Still, you expect that in a local derby; nowadays it's almost part of it.

I'd had a few of the old butterflies in the dressing-room; the first time, really, since I'd established myself in the team, but once the lads started hammering the ball in at me, they went away and I felt ready. I looked up the other end, and there was old Peter, The Cat. Someone put in a high one, and he got up to it and pulled it down. Jumped beautifully.

Then Jackie Noakes won the toss, we stayed at the Shed end, and Chelsea kicked off. There they all were, I thought, looking down-field. Peter Osgood, Charlie Cooke, Alan Hudson. Old 'Chopper' Harris and Webby in the defence. And of course, Peter Bonetti. This was the first time I'd ever hoped he'd play bad.

We made another good start. Chelsea were marking man to man at the time, and the Boss always fancied us against that kind of team. Like he said, all we had to do was lay the ball off first time and move into space. The other thing was the way we used Jesse Maude; we had him going on both wings, because he could move either way, he was completely two-footed, whereas the full-back who followed him around – in this case Webby, David Webb – might not be.

This time, Jesse started on the left, but early in the game he went out to the right, and I could see Chelsea were confused, you see a lot from goal. Webby went with him, but Eddie McCreadie, the other back, didn't seem quite sure who to take, because we weren't using another orthodox winger. What happened was that we had the man over. Jesse held it perfectly, waited till he was sure Danny would be onside, then he released it. Danny went after it to the line, pulled it back across goal, and Bob Cullen ran to the near post, got down to it, and headed it in. You could see the Borough scarves waving all over the ground, and they started this chant, 'Oh, now you've got to believe us, we're going to win the League,' which amused me a bit, coming this early.

That shook Chelsea a bit, and it was a quarter of an hour or so before they started coming back. When they did, Jackie Noakes fouled Peter Osgood on the edge of the box, and they got a free kick. The lads formed a wall, I told them where I wanted them to stand, and Harry Jackson stood there waving them into position. Ossie ran at the ball like he was going to slam it, though I was pretty sure he wouldn't; and he didn't. He jumped over the top, but Alan Hudson, who was following up, didn't shoot, either. Instead he lobbed it over the wall, to my right, and Webby came round the blind side and hit it. It was a hell of a shot, but I got one hand to it, and turned it over the bar.

At half-time, we were still one up, and the Boss was very pleased. He said, 'Keep laying it off, keep moving it about. They'll come at you the first ten minutes, and that should give you more space.'

He was right, like he usually was; they really did come at us; I reckon they'd had a pep talk at half-time. Charlie Cooke and Ossie had a couple of shots charged down, then someone, it may have been McCreadie, lobbed in a high one, and I went up for it with Ossie. I knew I'd be pushed to catch it, he's very powerful in the air, so I decided that I'd punch it, but as we went up, he caught me and I lost my bearings, that terrible feeling when you're in mid-air, you're sort of spinning, and you're helpless – though I *had* pushed the ball away, at least I knew that.

Next second I was down, bang, and everything went dark. When I come round Don Collins was bending over me with the old smelling salts, asking me, 'Are you all right, Ron?' I didn't know what to say to that, I expected him to tell *me*. At first it was hard to hear what he was saying then I did hear him, and after him the crowd.

It's terrible, lying there injured, and to a keeper, it happens so often. I mean, being hurt, being in pain, having treatment and that, should be a private thing, but there you are laid out in front of maybe fifty, sixty thousand people, and what's more, if you're away from home, people that don't want you to get up, that shout things at you like, '*He*'s all right' and 'Get him off the field, ref!' or a lot worse. You just have to try and shut them out.

But this one was bad, it was in the shoulder; what was worse, the right one. Don said, 'Try to move your arm,' and I did, but it was as stiff as hell. He felt it and said, 'You haven't dislocated. Think you can go on?' I said 'I'll try.' He asked, 'Want to come off for an injection? Kill the pain?'

I said, 'Only if it gets worse. Maybe it'll wear off.' He said, 'Don't forget; come off if you're in trouble,' then he stuck all his stuff back into his little white shoulder bag, and he was away.

I stood there in the goal rubbing my shoulder, wondering what was going to happen if they came down again, quickly. It was a free kick, and normally I'd take it, I'm a good dead ball kicker, I'd practise for hours, day in day out, but Jackie had to take this one. For high crosses, I didn't know what I'd do; punch them one-handed, I suppose; there wasn't a hope of catching them. But Ernie Leech was the substitute, and if I did go off, then who would they put in goal?

Luckily the lads kept play away from me the next five minutes or so, and though the shoulder went on aching, it wasn't so bad as it was. I could raise my arm to shoulder height, but any higher and it was murder.

Chelsea knew it of course, and the first time they got away, Ossie put in a lob. Normally I'd have eaten it, but this time all I could do was reach up to it with my left hand, the good one, and push it over the bar. I felt a right mug, I can tell you. But waiting for the corner to come over was worse; I felt so helpless. If I came out for it, like I usually do for corners, I couldn't try to catch it, I could only punch it, and with my left hand, at that. I don't think I've ever known a cross take longer coming over than that one did, it seemed to hang in the air forever – an inswinger, from Charlie Cooke, it was – and normally it would have been mine. I'd told the lads I'd probably stay on my line, and I did. The ball reached Ian Hutchinson, he jumped well, and he headed down, but I managed to get behind it, and I held it.

How I lasted the rest of that game, I'll never know, but I did. The defence was marvellous, Jackie Noakes and the others, they gave me wonderful protection, dropping back deeper than they normally would, which meant that Chelsea could push up further without the risk of being offside, but as things were, it was worth it. I held another shot from Ian Hutchinson, low enough for me to get both arms around it, then there was a header by Ossie that luckily went to my left hand, so I could tip it round the post.

I did go out to one cross from the left, their right, that was swinging away from me, and it was terrible. I felt completely off balance, completely defenceless, but just going for it, with my left arm up, was enough, because although Ian Hutchinson got it, it meant that he headed over the bar.

Then at the other end there was Bonetti, and I must say I admired him as much as I ever done, standing behind him on the terraces. He made some fabulous saves. There was one from Bob Cullen that was incredible. Bob got his head to a cross from Jesse, out on the left, and I could have sworn it was in, but Peter somehow did a back somersault and stopped it. I wanted to clap, myself. Watching him, his positioning, the way he could change direction on the ground, the way he held high crosses, made me realize how much there still was to learn. I knew I could never have done some of the things he did, even at my best.

Not having arms, so to speak, made me rely on my legs, and I was very glad I'd put in so much practice with these Continental saves – which was something Peter didn't use that much. Ossie was through once in a one-two with Hutchinson, but I'd seen it early and I was out very quick; he hardly hit it when I was in on him, and it bounced off my legs. He was dead choked, he said, 'Jammy so-and-so,' but I just laughed at him.

Towards the end they got a bit desperate and there was some hard stuff going on, but we held out, and when the whistle went it was still 1–0. All the lads come crowding round me, asking how I was, patting me on the back, but the thing I valued most of all was Peter Bonetti coming up to me as we went into the tunnel, patting me on the back and saying, 'Great game, son; the best one-handed goalkeeper I've seen for years.' I tried to answer, but I couldn't, there was such a lot I wanted to say to him, what he'd been to me when I was a kid, what it meant to play against him. How could you say all that?

Naturally once I got 'cold' the shoulder hurt all the more. The family was waiting outside the dressing-rooms afterwards to see how I was, all very anxious, especially Mum, but the Boss told her, 'Don't worry about him, Mrs Blake, he's all right, he'll be playing again next Wednesday!' and Mum said 'Oh, Mr Macintosh, please don't make him play again *too* soon!' then Don and Billy drove me over to St Stephen's hospital, in the Fulham Road, for an X-ray.

The X-ray showed nothing broken, just very severe bruising. Don said, 'Come over to Borough tomorrow morning, I'll get some heat on it,' but even after that, it was still very sore, there wasn't much movement, and I knew there wasn't a hope for Wednesday, when we had the return with Everton. I was right choked; it would be the first game I'd missed since I come into the team. On Monday the club doctor had a look at it, Doc Redding; a very good bloke, a big bloke, really knew his stuff and mucked in well with all the lads. He and Don went through all the clever stuff about traumas and ligaments and contusions and all the rest of it, till I asked, 'Think I'm going to live, Doc?'

He said, 'I'm afraid there's every possibility. But you won't be alive and well and playing at Everton.' Which depressed me, naturally. It's terrible to be injured, and of course if you're a goalkeeper, it's going to happen a lot, though generally speaking I'd been quite lucky. A lot of bruises, but so far, touch wood, never anything broken. I didn't go down to Snaresbrook, I just came into Borough in the afternoon for treatment. When the list went up on the Tuesday, naturally Terry Morgan was in, and I wished him luck. He said, 'Thanks, Ronnie,' but like he was a bit embarrassed. It's never nice, a situation like that; the bloke naturally wants your place, and naturally you want to keep it, to get it back. At the same time, for the team's sake, you want him to do well. And with a keeper, of course, there's only the one chance of getting back, just the one person you can displace.

We did all right up at Everton, drew 2–2, and apparently Terry had a fair game, though the papers I saw next morning seemed to think he might have had the second Everton goal, a header by Joe Royle, and so did some of the lads who came in for treatment on the Thursday. Graham Gibbs said, 'You'd have got it, Ronnie,' and I admit I felt chuffed about that. Still, there was no substitute for playing.

The other thing was I got more and more restless at home, and being so much at home, now, underlined it. I admit I wasn't all that easy to get on with, being injured. I felt like someone had put me in a straitjacket that however hard I fought to get out of it, I couldn't. It's terrible to be injured, when you earn your living with your arms and legs. Times like this, I think I realized what it must be like to be a cripple, though I reckon a cripple sort of learns to live with it, it's something that's with him all the time, whereas a footballer's fretting to get back in the game.

It wasn't that we had any quarrels at home, any up-and-downers. The old man's always liked a quiet life, and my mother, she doesn't often put her foot down; it was more the atmosphere, knowing what I wanted to do and couldn't, what the other lads could do that were in digs, or even married; feeling this uncomfortable feeling that I was earning so much, while he was earning so little. However much I chipped in, however little I spent myself, I couldn't get round that.

What I found myself doing was buying more and more stuff, bringing in fruit and that, odd clothes and things, but that didn't really work, either, because the old man obviously felt embarrassed if I got him things, even if it was just tobacco or a bottle of drink, while if he was there when I brought something in for Mum or for the house, he was all sort of on edge. He said to me one day, 'You don't have to do all this, Ron.'

I said, 'Why not, Dad? I like to.' He was looking away from me. He said, 'We don't want for nothing, son. You're a good boy, we're all very proud of you, you don't have to do no more than you're doing.'

I'd hoped I'd maybe be okay for the Saturday, we were at home to Newcastle United, but although I was getting the movement back, it still wasn't quite right. The old doc had a look at it, over in his consulting-room at the hospital, in Holloway. He said, 'There's two kinds of injured footballer; the malingerer and the optimist. You're an optimist.'

I said, 'Can you put it into English, Doc?' he said, 'The malingerer doesn't want to play. Or he may want to play, but he's a hypochondriac, who always thinks there's something wrong with him. The optimist *always* wants to play, even when he shouldn't, either because he's anxious, or because he can't belive there's anything wrong with him. I don't think you're anxious, though you're obviously anxious to *play*. But you're too young to believe you're really hurt.'

I said, 'Thanks, Doc, I'll try and work it out,' but he was certainly dead shrewd. It was amazing, some of the pros you'd find who actually preferred *not* to play, whereas me, I'd still play two games in a day if they wanted me to. Not that you found this in the Borough first team, because we were all young and keen but before, in the Reserves, I'd found it. I remember one of them, one of the older ones that had lost his place in the League side, getting off the treatment table when he'd been told he was fit and saying, 'That's the worst news I've had this week.' And sure enough he was back in again, on the Monday, with something else.

So I watched on the Saturday, and in a way I wished I hadn't. Naturally I wanted us to win, naturally I didn't want Terry to play badly, but at the same time, obviously, I was worried about my place. In fact he dropped a high cross in the first few minutes, and that was a funny feeling; first of all, I admit it, not being all that sorry that he'd done it, but in the same moment, being dead scared, all tight in my stomach, that they were going to put it in. In fact when the ball went loose Dyson had a shot at it, but Jackie Noakes blocked it.

On the other hand it was interesting to have a chance to watch us, from up in the stand, because it's a different game from there; everything laid out in front of you, all looking so neat and easy. You can see the open spaces, you can see who isn't marking, who's got into a bad position. Even when you're a goalkeeper, and you see more than anyone, you never get a view like that. The crowd certainly loved Danny, and he turned it on a few times, even if now and then he overdid it, taking on the extra man when he should have passed, or having a go at goal when someone else was better placed. Though they were different in style, Tommy

Dougall being more of the close dribbler, Scottish type, he and Tommy had this in common. Still, between them they certainly caused a lot of trouble, and eventually Tommy scored, he hit a lovely volley from the edge of the box, after Newcastle had headed out a corner.

In the second half Newcastle came into it a bit more. They were playing to Wyn Davies' head a lot, and I must say I didn't envy Terry playing against him, he was so tall and he got up to the ball so well. The only thing was that usually he liked to lay the ball off for someone else, he was very unselfish, which in a way gave you a second chance. I tried to work out how *I*'d have dealt with him, whether I'd have punched or whether I'd risk trying to catch it. Terry sometimes did one, sometimes the other, but there was a few occasions when he punched and didn't make proper contact, so there was a scramble before we got the ball away.

About five minutes from time, when it was still 1–0, Danny picked the ball up just inside his own half, glided past a couple of men, the way he can, and hit a lovely through ball for Bob Cullen. Bob went away very fast, he's got this tremendous acceleration. He shot, the keeper, Mc-Faul, blocked it but couldn't hold it, and Moncur was following up so fast it hit him and bounced into the net. It was a bit of a lucky goal in a way, but on the other hand we'd cut them apart, and we were worth it on the play.

I went down in the dressing-room to say well done to the lads. They were all very pleased, all laughing and singing in the bath, and of course I was pleased for them too. But it's a funny feeling when you haven't played, you feel like a bit of a layabout, they've done it all and you've only watch. I didn't know quite what to say to Terry Morgan, because if I said, 'Well played,' he might think I was taking the mickey, after those boobs he'd made early on. So I sort of nodded and smiled at him and said, 'All right, then, Terry?' very cheerful, and he smiled back.

Next Saturday, at Wolves, I was in again.

It was a few weeks after that that I fixed up to share digs with Bob Cullen. Bob wasn't too happy where he was, and I'd put it to the Boss about leaving home. He hadn't been that keen at first, he'd said, 'What's the matter? Won't they let you throw parties? Won't they let you bring your girl friends back?' I said, 'No, Boss, it's nothing like that.'

He said, 'I like my players living at home. Especially the young ones. It's a good atmosphere. It helps them keep the heid. Less temptations. You're very lucky to be *able* to live at home. You know how old I was when I went away? Fourteen. That's how old. Good cooking. People who want the best for you. I've met your father and mother; I like them.'

I said, 'I like them, and all; it isn't that.'

He said, 'Well, what is it?' and I didn't know how to tell him; I said, 'Well, for one thing, I'd like to be nearer the club.'

'Is that it?' he said. 'Is that all? How long does it take you to get here, now you've got a car? How long does it take you to drive to Snaresbrook? You know how old I was before *I* had a car? Twenty-eight. That's a fact. I'd walk everywhere. And I'll tell you something; it was better for me. I was healthier.'

I said, 'Yeah, well I can believe that, Boss, but even so I'd still like to move. I'd feel happier.' He said, 'Would your mother feel happier? Would your father feel happier?' But the end of it was that he told me to think it over, said *he*'d think it over, and if I still felt the same way after another month, maybe he'd arrange it.

Naturally I did feel the same, in fact I felt it more than ever. Nothing ever got said, but it was like the old man wasn't cock of his own walk no more. Not that I threw my weight around or nothing, in fact I was very careful not to, but there was times, for instance, when Mum would ask *me* things, in front of Dad, too, which normally she'd ask *him*.

Another thing was that when my eighteenth birthday came round, the lads and I had a bit of a party over at Jesse Maude's and Joe Lyons's digs. When I told them about it at home, their faces fell, because before, we'd usually done something there. My mother said, 'But we *always* have it at home, Ronnie,' and I said, 'Yes, I know, normally I still would, Mum. It was just that the lads invited me,' which they had. And the thing was that I couldn't invite the family as well, because it wasn't going to be that sort of party; a lot of the lads were bringing their girl friends, and one or two were coming with their wives; Mum and Dad would only have felt out of place.

I said, 'I thought maybe we'd all go out to dinner the night after, at that Italian place in Notting Hill Gate,' and they said yes, but they were obviously disappointed. But again, this was the trouble; you have your family and you have your football club, and in a way, if you see what I mean, that *is* your family; you live with one another all the time, you travel with one another, you get to know one another. So we had the party like we'd arranged, and I must say it went well. I took a girl called Jill I'd met, who worked in a boutique up in Soho. Nobody drank much, mostly beer, and some not even that, though the girls had a few shorts – and Tommy Dougall did – but it was great, the atmosphere was marvellous, and at the end, they brought in a surprise. They'd had a cake made, with green icing, marked out like a football pitch, and a goal as well, with a chocolate goalkeeper in it. And on the cake they'd had written, all in white icing, HAPPY BIRTHDAY RONNIE. KEEP ON KEEPING THEM OUT. With eighteen candles, naturally.

When I told Mum and Dad I was moving out, that was even worse than about the party. Mum started crying, she kept saying, 'Aren't you happy here, Ronnie? I thought you were happy here!' and I put my arm round her, I said, 'I *am* happy, Mum, I've always been happy, it's just that I want to live nearer the ground,' to which she said exactly what the Boss had said, 'But you've got the car.'

What surprised me was that the old man came in on my side, he said, 'Ron's living a man's life now, dear, it's natural that he'd want to be with the other players; they're his friends, they're his world,' but there was no comforting Mum. She said she was afraid I wouldn't get enough to eat, that when I got ill there'd be no one to take care of me, and in the end I had to promise that I'd let her come up once a week and cook a meal for me and Bob Cullen.

When she went out to the kitchen, still with her handkerchief in her hand, the old man said, 'That's all right, Ron, I understand, there aren't no hard feelings.' So that was it. A week later I moved in with Bob, over at Muswell Hill.

I admit it was a strange feeling at first. The house we had digs in was quite a nice one, garden back and front, both of us with our own rooms, a lounge with a television. The woman that owned it was a widow, Mrs Cummings. She had a son of nine who was a Borough fan, and a daughter seven. She was great, she'd do anything for you; she'd been looking after Borough players for years. When Mum came over, they got on quite well; she told me afterwards she was used to dealing with mothers, but when Mum asked could she come over now and then and cook me a meal, she said, 'Don't worry, Mrs Blake, I'll feed him properly; there'll be no complaints, I promise you.' I noticed the first few times I come home for a meal Mum looking at me, like she was afraid I was fading away, but after a while she stopped worrying, she could see I was okay, and anyway, like she said, 'At least I can get a couple of good meals down you, every week.'

Bob and I got on well, he was very easy going, laughed a lot. We liked the same kind of television programmes, comedy and Westerns, mostly; we went out now and then with a couple of birds, and above all it was great to be able

133

to talk football all the time with somebody that really knew it, someone that was playing in your own side. I could honestly never get enough of that. At home, the old man always liked to discuss it, of course, but it couldn't be the same; not that he was ignorant of anything, but simply that he was outside it all, there were a lot of things you just couldn't explain to him.

The same went for Mike, when I ran into him, or when he came round which he still did now and then. Only with Mike it was more difficult, because he still fancied himself a lot on what he knew, besides which, he'd given me all that advice when I was younger.

One day when I was home, I ran into him in Ladbroke Grove, and we went for a drink; he padlocked the old bike to a Belisha beacon. He had a beer. I just had a lemonade; you'd be amazed the way people get on to the club if they see you in a pub, even if all you've got in your hand's a half of shandy. We'd just drawn at home with Tottenham, it had been a right old London derby, very fast, very hard, very even; a bit disappointing for us, because we were higher in the table than the Spurs, but still, we hadn't lost it.

Mike said, 'That cross, Ronnie, the one the goal came from, you should have had it before it even reached Gilzean,' who was the one that scored. And I got a bit stroppy, I said, 'A goalkeeper can't get everything, Mike.'

And he put on that smile of his I knew so well, the 'I know better than you do' one, he said, 'But, Ron, that ball couldn't have been more than ten yards out.'

'No, it wasn't, Mike,' I said. 'It was nearer fifteen, and anyway, to me it was a defender's ball. It should have been Jackie Noakes, who was taking Gilly.'

'Ronnie,' he said, in this ever so *reasonable* voice he put on, 'a ball that near to goal can't be Jackie's ball, it can't be *anybody*'s ball but yours. The first duty of any goalkeeper is he's got to command his area, and besides, a shortish bloke like Jackie is always going to be in trouble jumping with a tall bloke like Gilzean, especially one that gets up so well.'

'If what you're saying's true,' I said, 'you wouldn't need any defenders in the box at all; they could just clear out and leave it all to the goalkeeper.'

'There's no need to get aggressive, Ron,' he said. 'You know that's not what I meant. Of course you need defenders in the box. What *you're* saying is you don't need a goalkeeper.'

'Okay, Mike,' I said. 'You know best. You always know better than anyone.'

'Ronnie,' he said, then, 'I'm disappointed in you. You've changed. You were never like this as a kid. You used to be able to take criticism. What's come over you, Ron? All this big time stuff? You're still only a kid. You've still got things to learn.'

'I know that,' I said, 'and I know who I can learn them from,' and as soon as I said it, I felt sorry that I had, because he didn't mean no harm, old Mike, I realized that afterwards. It was simply his way.

He nodded then, he said, 'All right. All right, Ron. If that's the way you feel,' and he got up. I asked him did he want another beer, but he said no. He said, 'Just think about what I told you,' then he went out. I waited till he must be gone, then I went, too.

It was a shame, that, but everything was still happening so fast that I hadn't much time to think about it. We were top of the League, there was all this stuff in the papers about us, BOROUGH'S BABES, and all that rubbish. You got the feeling that half the reporters wanted us to go on doing well, because it gave them something to write about, and the other half wanted us to blow up. Then there were blokes like Arthur Bright, on the *Gazette*, who it was all the same to whether you won or lost. If you were up, they were on your side, if you went down, they were the ones that put the boot in.

This was the bloke they called the Man in the Black Homburg, the lads had warned me when I got into the team, 'Watch him,' but at first he hadn't taken any notice of me, though he'd put a few quotes in I was meant to have said, just the same. Then when I started getting a bit of publicity he was quite friendly, bought me a beer now and then, asked me how I was, and that, though I notice he didn't seem too interested in the answer.

He was there the day we lost our first match, away to West Bromwich, up at The Hawthorns. They got a couple of quick goals, Jeff Astle getting up well to head them back, Tony Brown coming in fast and belting them, and although Danny knocked one in before half-time, we were never really in it. In the dressing-room, the Boss gave us a tremendous hammering, rollicking Tommy Dougall for not picking up Tony Brown, getting at Ray McGraw for allowing Jeff Astle to beat him in the air.

Ray didn't say anything, he was usually very quiet, though he could be hard on the field. But Tommy wouldn't have it, he tried to give the Boss an argument, he said, 'You can't blame anyone for goals like that, they were just well taken goals.' The Boss said, 'Yes, you can! I *am*! I'm blaming *you*!' Tommy said, 'Well, *I* don't accept it,' and the Boss did his nut, he started shouting at him, telling him *he* was the manager of this club, and if Tommy didn't do what he said, he could find himself another team. Tommy said, in a very quiet voice that I wasn't sure the Boss could hear, 'Maybe I will,' then it blew over. I'd never seen the Boss get so steamed up; to me, there was right on both sides, but like the Boss said, rollicking Tommy, 'There's no such thing as a good goal against you! Every goal is given away by somebody's error!'

The second half hadn't been going ten minutes when we gave away another. This time Asa Hartford got it, he hit a terrific half-volley through a crowd of players, and I never even saw it, I was completely unsighted. Joe Lyons kicked the ball out of the back of the net and said, 'Well, that's it,' and it was. Tommy more or less dropped out of the game, Danny got clobbered once or twice and was obviously struggling, and when we did get a half chance, near the end, Bob Cullen put it over the bar. When the final whistle went, I was dreading going back in that dressing-room, I can tell you, but when the Boss came down, all he said was, 'Well, it had to happen some time, but it shouldn't have happened today.' Nobody said much; we were all too choked.

Three or four London reporters got on our coach to go to the station; one of them was Arthur Bright, the black homburg bloke, the other was a funny looking fellow who wrote for one of the posh Sunday papers, Dudley Welsh, that the boys all seemed to like. To me, he looked like some old actor, the old-fashioned coats he wore, his looks, his voice, and he could knock back the drink, I'll certainly say that. He came and sat next to me; I noticed that Arthur Bright was sitting next to Tommy Dougall who was all hunched up, very morose. I heard him say, 'Commiserations, commiserations,' and Tommy answered something back. I couldn't hear what it was, but judging by his expression, it wasn't too cheerful.

This Dudley Welsh said to me, 'You poor young fellow. You were cruelly abandoned today. Left all alone, in the imminent, deadly breach.' I could smell the whisky on his breath, 'Can't win 'em all,' I said.

He laughed, like I'd said something very funny, and he said, 'Never mind; you're young. The world is your oyster! Life's a bowl of cherries! Eat them; but don't swallow the stones!'

I didn't know what to say to that, what could you say? But he seemed a friendly enough bloke, there was nothing stuck-up about him, for all the way he talked, and when he began discussing the game, he obviously knew what he was on about, which is more than you can say for quite a few of them. He asked me had I been unsighted for that third goal, and did I think we'd been too busy watching Jeff Astle and forgotten Brown, but they weren't the usual reporter's questions, just niggling away, trying to get you to say something; he really seemed to be interested.

He started talking about other goalkeepers, and it was good listening to him, some of them keepers I'd seen, some I'd heard of that were before my time, like Frank Swift and Bert Williams, others, mostly foreigners, that I'd never heard of at all. When he mentioned one that had played before the war, Harry Jackson, who was sitting across the aisle, said, 'Watch it, Dudley, you'll be giving yourself away!' and Dudley Welsh said, 'My dear boy, I'm *always* trying to give myself away; the trouble is, no one will have me!'

On the train, in the dining-car, there wasn't a lot said. The cards came out, at least it was something to distract you, and after that, there was the meal. I noticed Tommy didn't join in the card game; he sat in a corner reading a book, with Arthur Bright on the same table. He was drinking, they both were – the Boss never minded, after a game – but they didn't seem to be talking a lot. Tommy read quite a lot of books, the rest of us didn't bother much; personally I'd never really got into the habit.

There were quite a few supporters on the train, walking through the diner, stopping to talk to us, asking for autographs, and I must say this was one of the times you could have done without them, the questions they asked, like, 'What went wrong, Ronnie?' I heard Ray McGraw say to one of them, 'They got three and we got one, that's what went wrong. Now buzz off!'

Dudley Welsh came and stopped by our table once, he was carrying a glass of whisky and he seemed well away. He said, 'Courage, my old companions! One defeat doesn't make a disaster! The title can still be yours!'

Jesse Maude said, 'Think so, Dudley?' and he said, 'Think so, dear boy? I know so! And I shall drink a toast:

138

to Borough's chances of the Championship!' Jesse said, 'I'll drink to that,' and we all did, then Dudley bought us a round of beers. Jesse said, 'A gentleman; a human being.'

That Monday, it was all over the back of the *Gazette*; TOMMY DOUGALL SLAMS MANAGER MACINTOSH. The usual old load of rubbish, how Tommy was cheesed off at being blamed for the defeat, how he reckoned the Boss was making him a scapegoat and he was going in to ask for a transfer. Some of it sounded like he might have said it, some of it you could tell was Arthur Bright, because he always wrote the same way, it didn't matter whether he was meant to be quoting a footballer or some jockey; all this, 'I tell you, Arthur, Borough's no place for me under Manager Macintosh's oh-so-authoritarian regime.'

Bob Cullen and I read it over the breakfast table, and some of it we laughed at and some of it we wondered about. I asked Bob, 'Do you reckon he said it?' and Bob said, 'Some of it, probably. You don't need to say much for this bloke to blow it up into a story,' and I said, 'They were sitting together on the coach and in the train. Maybe Tommy reckoned it was all off the record.'

Bob said, 'Nothing's off the record with that fellow. If he told him anything, he was a mug.' Because generally speaking, when you're with a reporter, especially one you know quite well, you can let off steam without worrying, he'll know it's not for publication. But there's just a few, mostly the young ones coming up and trying to make themselves a name, and one or two right baskets like this Arthur Bright, who'll drop you in it.

Down at Snaresbrook, you could feel it all in the air. Tommy wasn't saying anything, he was very quiet, and the Boss wasn't looking at Tommy. In the dressing-room, some one had said, 'They pay you well for that article, Tom? Enough to pay the fine?' and Tommy said, 'They didn't pay me a so-and-so penny.' That was all. After training, the Boss called Tommy over and they both went into the little

139

office that he used, there. I expected to see the walls shaking, because they were both Scots, they could both do their nuts at times, but in fact there wasn't a sound and when Tommy came out he didn't say a word, he just walked straight out of the building, got into his car and drove away.

It was Billy Wallis that told us what happened. He said, 'Tom's suspended.' So that evening he made the papers again; he'd been suspended for a fortnight and fined – we heard it was fifty quid. After that there was a lot of paper talk about how he'd said he'd never kick another ball for Borough, but the long and short of it was, when the fortnight was up, there he was at Snaresbrook again, like nothing had happened, and the Boss was very friendly to him. They're hard to understand at times, Scotsmen, one minute scrapping, the next all pals. Still, I was glad to see him back, myself. We hadn't looked so good while he was away; dropped a point at home to Southampton, then drawn again, at Leicester.

But although we started playing well again, beating Manchester United, picking up a point at Arsenal, it wasn't quite the same. Maybe it was just me, I don't know, because till then, everything had gone so smoothly. But I felt the difference in the whole team. Whereas before everybody had been pulling together, everyone behind the Boss, now, you could feel there were undercurrents. Tommy himself, he'd always been ready to moan about a professional footballer this, a professional footballer that, but now when he did, it somehow sounded more personal.

'Everything done for you,' he'd say. 'All your planning; all your thinking. They even tell you how you ought to play.' Which was a bit thick, really, coming from Tommy, who nobody could tell how to play, because once he had the ball at his feet, he couldn't tell you what he was going to do, himself; until he'd done it. But it was true the Boss didn't exactly encourage you to disagree with him in the team talks. When he said, 'Any questions?' he meant had you understood what he'd told you, not had you got any ideas of your own – which Tommy usually had.

To me, this didn't matter very much, because I was so young, I was still learning – in fact I'd have been in the England youth team that season and the one before, if Borough hadn't needed me for the League side – and I was happy to be playing at all. For people like Tommy, though, who'd played international, it was a bit different, but after this West Bromwich thing, I noticed he didn't have so much to say at team talks; though anyone could see when he disagreed, the smile he put on, like he was sorry for anyone that stupid. The Boss would give him an old-fashioned look now and again, but they seemed to be steering clear of one another, now.

When Christmas came we were still on top of the League, a point ahead of Leeds, and three ahead of Manchester United. We played West Ham twice, two good games, the first time I'd played against Geoff Hurst, which wasn't easy, believe me. He was like Astle, the way he got up to a high ball, ever so strong he was, you could never shift him, and he had a terrific thump in either foot. One shot he banged at me at Upton Park, it must have been from a good twenty yards out, looked easy till I came to take it – then it was travelling so fast that it hit me on the chest and bounced out of my arms. Luckily it bounced past their forwards following up, too. But we got a point there, and did them 2–1 at home, so we still kept our noses out in front.

Then it was the Cup, the Third Round, and we were drawn away to Tranmere Rovers, the worst sort of draw you could have. A big team like us was on a hiding to nothing, while a little Fourth Division team like theirs had nothing to lose. On their own ground, they were bound to come at us like lunatics and I don't think any of us was much looking forward to it; though to me, it had to be exciting, being my first Cup-tie. I only hoped it wasn't going to be my last one; at least for this season.

The Boss was on at us a lot about taking it seriously. He told us, 'Walsall beat the Arsenal, in 1933.' (Danny said, 'I missed that one, Boss.') He said, 'And Colchester United knocked out Leeds in 1971; Fourth Division against First Division. So don't think it canna happen to us. They'll do what Colchester did against Leeds, they'll throw everything at us; there's no other way. They'll try and hustle us off our game. They'll give us no time to think. They'll pump long balls into the area. They'll put pressure on Ronnie.'

Arthur Prescott, our right-back, said, 'Blimey, Boss, what'll *we* do? Hide?' He said, 'Hide's the last thing we'll do. Anyone who hides will have to answer to me. I've no time for cowards on a football field, especially in a match like this. If they're physical, we've got to be more physical. If they're hard, we've got to be harder.'

Harry Jackson asked, 'Do we play any football, Boss?' and he said, 'Of course we play football. But we play simple football. One-touch football. We lay it off. We don't get caught in possession. We break fast out of defence. We use long balls; we exploit Bob Cullen's speed. I want a result down there; I dinna want to be bothered with a replay.'

Well, we weren't, but not in the way he wanted. To begin with, it was a terrible day, the rain had come down in buckets in the night; we knew all about it where we were, in Liverpool, and even before we started off for Tranmere, there was a gloomy sort of atmosphere, like everybody knew things were going to go wrong. Not just the usual tension you get before a match; something more than that. A few supporters rolled up in the middle of the morning, rich ones, the kind that were always asking the lads out to this do and that do, taking them over to the Sportsman's Club in the West End, and that, quite nice blokes, really, one called Harry Kerman, another called Jack Aaron. They were wearing their Borough scarves and rosettes, which always looked a bit ridiculous to me with the other gear they had, posh suits and pricey coats and that.

Jack Aaron came and sat next to me, he was a youngish bloke, in property or something, drove about in a big Bentley, but he loved to think he was one of the boys. 'All set, then, Ronnie?' he says, which is the kind of question that annoys me, what happens if you say, 'No'? I said, 'Yeah, all ready, Jack,' and he says, 'That's the stuff.' Then we sit there and neither of us says anything, because I can't think of anything to say, and he's obviously waiting for me to say something. In the end what he says is, 'Why don't you come up to the Hilton with me on Monday week, Ronnie, as my guest? See the boxing. We'll have a good evening. Jesse Maude's coming.'

I said, 'Well, yeah, thanks, Jack, can I let you know?' because by now it had worn off, all this Hilton stuff and the clubs. The boxing wasn't usually all that, I didn't like drinking, and I felt a bit like Tommy Dougall did about it – though he went quite often. He'd said, 'You're there like a performing dog. They say, "Beg," and you stand up and beg, then they throw you another biscuit.' So in the end the two of us sat there, this fellow and I, not saying a word, till he got up and said, 'Well, good luck, Ronnie,' and went away to look for someone else. There's all kinds of hangers-on in football, some of them rich, some of them poor, but like Tommy once said, 'They've got one thing in common, they all of them want something from you.'

The coach ride there wasn't all that, anyway, the rain slopping down against the windows, the light very bad, everyone wondering whether the game would be put off, and I think half hoping that it would. We could imagine what the pitch was going to be like, and when we got there – it was. Walking around on it before the game, you could hardly stand up in your ordinary shoes, you went squelching through the wet, there were great puddles everywhere, and you could tell how it was going to churn up. They'd put sawdust down in the penalty areas, but the rate things were going on, I didn't think that was going to help much.

Danny looked at it like he was right disgusted, he said, 'If I'd known it was going to be like this, I'd have brought me snorkel,' and the Boss turned to me in the goalmouth and said, 'Never mind, Ronnie; if you're in real trouble, I'll be out in the lifeboat!' I laughed, but to me it didn't seem all that funny.

And it was a terrible game; it couldn't have been anything else. You certainly hadn't a chance of playing football on it. Players were sliding all over the park on their backsides, the ball was sticking in a puddle one moment, and shooting like mad the next. I went out to dive at a through ball early in the match that the centre-forward was coming after, got it all right, then nearly slid right out of the penalty area, in the mud. I got up all filthy, mud on my shorts and jersey, my gloves all covered with mud, it was diabolical.

They came at us like the Boss had said they would, and you had to give them credit, they were very determined. Early on you could see it wasn't going to be Danny or Tommy's day, a ball player's, because the only thing to do was shift it, if you tried to hang on, you just got yourself stuck in the mud. Danny got caught in possession like that a couple of times early on, the second with a very hard tackle; he went down and had to have treatment. The Boss was right, too, when he said they'd use a lot of high balls, and they weren't easy, because the ball got so slippery. You didn't dare try to catch it, you had to punch, and even then you couldn't be sure where it was going to go.

Which was how they got a goal, after twenty minutes or so. One of their players, the right-back, I think it was, hit a long, high ball into the box. I went up for it with a couple of their forwards, and I was definitely impeded, there's no doubt about it, but it's the sort of thing you can never be sure you'll get, especially when you're playing away. So though I did get the ball, it skidded off the top of my knuckles, it didn't quite reach the edge of the penalty area; one of them volleyed it, and I'd got no chance of getting back. Joe Lyons went up to it, but it only hit the top of his head and went on into the goal. There was about the loudest roar I'd ever heard; in a little ground like that, they're all breathing down the back of your neck, anyway.

Naturally that gave them a tremendous boost, like it always does when a little team scores against a big one. They hadn't got a lot of skill, but on a day like this it didn't matter very much; if you tried to bring off anything clever, you either finished on your back or the ball stuck in the mud. By the time it was half-time, I'd had just about enough of rolling about in the mud with boots coming in at me from all over the place. I'd had to turn one shot round the post, point-blank, and another time I made these terrible conditions work for me, because I came slithering out to block one with my legs that ordinarily I probably wouldn't have reached. That was when Jackie Noakes slipped and one of their forwards was right through.

I knew what we were in for when we got into that little dressing-room, and we were; the Boss was calling us everything under the sun, said we were playing into their hands by holding the ball, that we had to move it long, we had to use the wings, where there was still a bit of firm going. He said to me, 'And as for you, Ronnie, you'll have to let 'em know you're there. You'll get nothing from this referee, he's terrified, he's a homer.'

I said, 'I'm doing what I can, Boss,' and he said, 'Well, you'll have to do more. You'll have to go right through them. Come in with your knees up. He won't penalize you, not the goalkeeper.'

When we got out there again it was still pelting down, still miserable. We tried to do what he'd said, using Jesse Maude on the left-wing and Bob Cullen down the right.

Once Bob made a lovely run, he went past two men beautifully on the outside and crossed. The keeper dived out for it, made a mess of it, the ball came straight to Graham Gibbs, following up, but as Graham went to hit it, he slipped, and that was that. I knew then we'd never do it. It was one of those games that the harder you try, the less chance you've got.

They tired towards the end, which was understandable, and we put on quite a lot of pressure, but they had practically the whole team around their own penalty box, and in those conditions, there wasn't any getting through. I was sick, I can tell you; my first Cup-tie, and we'd lost it. Millions of kids, their supporters, came running on to the field at the final whistle, and I ran through them as quick as I could, just touched their goalkeeper's hand, going down the tunnel, said, 'Well done,' but it didn't come easy, I can tell you.

When we got in the dressing-room we just sat there, not saying a word, we were completely shattered. For myself, I was so choked I wasn't even worried what the Boss would say, because it couldn't be worse than what I was feeling. My first Cup-tie, and this had to happen. In fact I put my head in my hands, and I admit I was crying. Graham Gibbs come up and put his hand on my shoulder, he said, 'Cheer up, Ron. We can concentrate on the League now!' and Bob Cullen was nice about it, too. But it didn't do any good, a Cup-tie's a Cup-tie, there's nothing like the Cup. Every player wants to play at Wembley, every player wants to win a Cup medal, and it was no use telling me I was still young, that I'd got twenty years to do it. Now was now, we were out for this year, and there was no changing that.

Most of the lads were dead nackered, after running around in that muck, and when the Boss come in and looked at us, I think he realized it. He looked like he could kill somebody, but in the end all he said was, 'Forget it all till Monday. And anyone that talks to the Press is fined a hundred pounds.' Then he went out. It wasn't too encouraging, I must say, but at least he hadn't rucked us. One of the lads said, in the bath, 'They'll have fun with this, the Press,' and Jackie Noakes said, 'Well, I'm not buying no Sunday papers tomorrow.'

Harry said, 'You can write it yourself, can't you? Borough Babes Crash at Tranmere.' Tommy Dougall said, 'Giant Killers Knock out Useless United,' and Danny said, 'Shut up, will you?' There were tears in his eyes; it was his first Cup-tie, too.

If the trip home from West Bromwich had seemed like a funeral, this was worse, this was like a graveyard, and it went on longer. The Boss just sat there with a face like Dracula. We'd heard him talking to the Press just before we left the ground, out in the dressing-room corridor, telling them he didn't want them speaking to any of us. He was saying, 'Why did we lose? Why do *you* think we lost? You saw the game, didn't you? You saw the conditions. It wasnae football. It should never have been played.'

Then on the train this bloke Jack Aaron come up to him, still wearing his scarf, and asked, 'What happened?' and I thought the Boss was going to get up and hit him. He said, 'What do *you* think happened? We lost, that's what happened! Have you got any more ridiculous questions?' Jack Aaron sort of gulped at him, then he sloped off.

As for the reporters, they kept away from him, except for Dudley Welsh, who came wandering through the diner in his tatty old coat, well away, as usual. He stopped by the Boss and said, 'My dear Charlie; you look like Napoleon after the retreat from Moscow! Forget it! Remember that the little old Corporal came back. He astonished everyone,' and the Boss said, 'Ay, but he still didnae win the Championship.'

'Never mind,' Dudley said, 'I shall send you over a glass of Napoleon brandy; if they have any on this little old restaurant car.' Then he came past our table and to me he said, 'My poor custodian; we always meet at wakes! Never mind; one day we shall meet at a banquet!' and swayed off down the train.

In fact we did pick up after that. The very next Saturday we won away at Stoke, who were going through a bad time then. We didn't play well, and the only goal came late in a breakaway, Bob Cullen got it, but who cared, it was still two points. Leeds, who were still out in front, had won in the Cup, they were in the European Cup as well, so we'd got hopes that maybe they'd fall down between the three, like they had a few years back. We went on winning, they went on winning, till in the end it all come down to what happened at Easter. We had a Saturday match with them at Elland Road, and a home game with Forest on the Monday.

We had Wally Evans in the side for Harry Jackson, who was having trouble with his knee, and Ernie Leech playing instead of Jesse Maude, who'd been going through a bit of a bad spell. Ernie was a good whole-hearted player, he'd chase anything and he wasn't afraid to take knocks, but he was basically a striker, a centre-forward, which left us without an orthodox winger – even if it allowed Tommy Dougall to move out on to the wings a lot, and of course Bob Cullen always liked working down the right.

For myself, as a goalkeeper, I've got a lot of respect for wingers, real ones, because they're the only people who can take the fullback on, go to the line, and pull the ball back, which any goalkeeper will tell you is the most dangerous pass in the game. I agreed that there was no point having Jesse in while he was out of touch, but I was sorry we'd got nobody else, no other winger.

In this game, anyway, the Boss was all taken up with stopping Terry Cooper coming down the left-wing on the overlap, so what he wanted was for Ernie Leech to play on the right more as an extra defender, stopping Terry Cooper coming through, and then breaking himself, if he won the ball. Tommy Dougall didn't say anything at the team talk, but afterwards he said, 'If we're going to be that negative, why don't we all of us just line up in the goalmouth, then if we win the ball, we can break in a line.'

I saw his point a bit, because in modern football you can't win, not as a goalkeeper. Either you're playing at home and attacking all the time, so that when the other side breaks away and has a shot you're cold, or else the home team's putting on the pressure and you've got so many bodies in your penalty area you're lucky if you even see the ball before it's on you; then as likely as not it's going to hit someone and be deflected.

Which was what happened at Leeds. We were on the defensive practically from the kick-off. They were playing really well, Billy Bremner and Johnny Giles running everywhere in midfield, Lorimer and Gray belting down the wings, Jackie Charlton coming up for the free-kicks and corners so you had him and Jones and Clarke all to worry about when the ball was in the air, let alone when he stood bang in front of you at the corners. Once he got a touch to the ball before I did, a back header, but Ray McGraw got up like a good 'un and just back headed it away himself. Another time Jones nodded one back to Clarke and he hit a tremendous volley; I threw myself for it, just touched it, didn't know whether I'd got enough deflection on it, but then I heard it smack against the post, and fortunately Graham Gibbs was rushing back and belted it behind for a corner.

As far as our attack was concerned, we just weren't in it. The only chance, as far as I could see, was that they were going to throw so many men upfield that in the end Bob Cullen, who could really shift, would get on to a long ball, and be right through on his own. It did nearly happen once, just after half-time I thought Bob was away, but Charlton pulled him back, and a free kick's no use to you, not in midfield.

At half-time the Boss was pleased, but Tommy wasn't, I could see by the way he was sitting, head down, all glowering. He hated playing in this kind of game, he used to say it wasn't football, which I suppose it wasn't. Danny wasn't enjoying it too much, either. In fact, I could see a change in Danny since he'd come into the team and everything had gone like a bomb. He was getting clobbered a lot now, people had got on to him, they were trying to intimidate him, kick him out of the game, and it's very hard, that kind of thing, for a young kid. Plus the fact that in a match like this, a player like Danny can't really express himself.

After half-time, it went on pretty much the same way; a hard game, lots of fouls, them attacking, us keeping them out.

We must have been playing about ten minutes when Terry Cooper came down on the overlap. Ernie Leech went with him but he beat him, he's got a very quick turn, then he beat Graham Gibbs, and then he crossed. It was a very good one, fast, a foot or two above the ground, and I could see it was coming to Jones, which to me meant he was going to hit it right-footed. I reckoned I knew where it would go, and even about what height. I was ready for it; he was about fifteen yards out, and I thought I could probably turn it over the top, but just as it reached him and he hit it, Ray McGraw lunged in on it, it hit him on the foot, and spun off like a maniac. I'd got no chance, I tried to change direction, I even managed to touch it with one hand, which wasn't bad, but I was right off balance, and I couldn't stop it going in. That was it; that was the goal we lost by.

In the train, Tommy Dougall was moaning a lot, saying, 'If we're going to lose, why not go down playing football? Why not go at them and try to beat them?' and Jackie Noakes, who never said much, gave a little sour smile and said, ' 'Cause we'd lose ten.'

'No, we wouldn't,' Tommy said, 'we might not lose at all.

Those two big fellows in the middle are vulnerable. If you catch their defence on the turn, you can murder them,' and Jackie said, 'Got to catch them first.'

But we all knew that was it for the League. Leeds were five points out in front now, and although we'd got a game in hand, it was still five points; it's the psychological thing. The Boss wasn't too choked about it, I suppose he couldn't be, seeing that we'd played his tactics. His line was that we'd lost to a streaky goal; he told the reporters. 'The luckiest goal I've seen for years. They could have gone on playing forever and not scored,' and Danny said under his breath, 'So could we.'

So we ended the season with nothing, third, which was a great place for such a young team, I suppose. The Directors were chuffed about it, I believe Charlie Macintosh got a rise, but when you hoped you were going to win the League, it wasn't much consolation.

I must confess that in the bad times, like that game at West Bromwich, the Cup-tie at Tranmere, I missed being at home, with the old man saying, like, 'Cheer up, you've got plenty to look forward to,' and Mum coming in with cups of tea. Whereas in digs, there was just Bob and me looking at each other across a table and making each other worse. The old girl that looked after us was nice, she was sympathetic, but there wasn't much she could do; and as for birds, you couldn't talk to them, they weren't interested in football, and the ones that were were mostly scrubbers.

Things perked up at the end of the season when we went on the England Under 23 tour, though, Danny and I; Milan, Strasbourg, and Basel. I won't say they were three of the most exciting places I'd ever been to, I was getting used to travelling now, but it was great to be picked, to get just that bit nearer the full England team; and with Danny about, there was always some fun. The funniest thing was to see him trying to chat up birds that didn't speak English, especially in Italy, where Danny's idea was just to put an 'a' or an 'o' on the end of the English words, and hope for the best. He didn't get anywhere in Italy, Basel was hard, too, but Strasbourg was a little bit better.

The bloke in charge of the tour was Ron Greenwood, the West Ham United manager, and what we noticed was how very, very different he was from Charlie Macintosh. He certainly knew the game; he could talk tactics till your head went round, but he was very quiet with it, too, smiled a lot, and if you wanted to say something, he encouraged it, even if he didn't agree. I suppose it was about then that Danny and I realized the Boss's way wasn't the only way, because it was the only way we'd been used to, growing up with it from juniors.

He gave me quite a few tips, Ron, especially on how to spot when a Continental was going to 'bend' a ball from the way he hit it, and also how to know whether a forward was going to shoot or pull it back, when he came in on you at the near post. This was something I was very grateful for, because you can look a right clown if you move out for the cross and he slips it just between you and the post; which nearly happened to me in Milan.

I was very interested in the way the Italians played. Though we had the game under floodlights it was still very, very hot, the ball was light, the ground was hard, but they controlled it beautifully. For about twenty minutes our boys got a right old run around, and I had to make two or three saves, but what I did notice was that when it came to physical contact, we were winning nearly everything. When they couldn't score, it seemed to depress them, and by the end we were well on top. It was 0–0, but to me, we were a bit unlucky not to win.

I didn't play the next game, in Basel, which we won 2–1, but I played in Strasbourg, against the French. It was a nice city, that. They took us round it on a tour and I enjoyed it, the old churches, more than Milan, which was stinking hot, and seemed to have just the cathedral, and Basel, where I don't know what they had. Danny didn't even like Strasbourg, though, he hated going on these tours, he'd always be the last one out of the coach, saying, 'Have I *got* to come, Mr Greenwood? Does my place depend on it?' and Ron Greenwood would say, 'Of course it does.'

We drew 2–2 with the French, they were quite lively, fannied around a lot on the ball, but with one or two forwards who could hit it. We were behind twice but came back twice, which wasn't bad. Danny got the second equalizer, but personally I wasn't too pleased with myself. I thought maybe I should have had their second, I should have seen it all a bit quicker. When I said that to Danny afterwards he said, 'Yeah, I know, but don't tell Ron; say you were unsighted!'

It was interesting, being with a lot of fellows from other clubs, blokes you'd played against but never talked to. You got to hear a lot about what went on elsewhere, how managers behaved, what people were getting paid, which was the main thing we talked about. This club paid crowd bonuses, that one paid according to League position, others had a high basic and not much in the way of bonuses. You could see some of the lads that were with poorer clubs, or ones in the Second Division, with their tongues hanging out when they heard what some of us were getting. One of them, with a Northern First Division team that hadn't got much money, said he'd put in for a transfer twice, but his contract had two years to run, and his club wouldn't let him go. He said, 'If they won't transfer me, I'm not going to kill myself,' which shocked me a bit.

I'd heard about it before, this playing to get away from a club, but this was the first time I'd actually come across it, and I knew I just couldn't do it, I loved the game so much. Fancy letting in a goal you knew you could have stopped; though I admit for a goalkeeper it's a bit different, because if he lets himself make a mistake, that's it.

153

I mentioned that I was shocked to Danny, but he said, 'I don't know. What else can he do?' I said, 'But you wouldn't, would you. Danny?' He said, 'If I was him, I might.' It sounded strange, coming from Danny; it reminded me a bit of the old sweats we'd had in the Reserves when I played for them, but that was different, they were mostly over the hill, where Danny was at the beginning.

I learned a few new card games, too; most of the clubs had their own favourites, some played aces and kings like us, some played a special kind of whist, there was solo, cribbage, the lot. It all passed the time, all that sitting about in hotels and airports, and I could have done without the official receptions, too, us all dressed up in our blazers, standing around and saying nothing, or having to answer stupid questions from reporters who hardly spoke English.

The Continentals obviously appreciated Danny a lot; it suited his game, because he got more time; he could do things that he'd never risk in a League match, because he knew he'd be flattened.

When I got home, there was this feeling again of hanging in the air, not really knowing what to do with your time, especially as Bob Cullen had gone home to Suffolk. We'd talked about going to Majorca together, like a lot of the footballers do, but nothing came of it, and in the end I went off with the family to Broadstairs.

I stuck four days of it, then I went to Majorca by myself. It was all right there, in Palma, quite a lot of footballers, nice birds, I enjoyed it. I came back looking forward to the season.

Chapter 4

With a goalkeeper, half of it is confidence. Obviously you've got to have something to be confident *about*, you've got to have the reflexes, you've got to have a good idea of angles, and that, but if your confidence goes, that's it; until you get it back. When it does go, and before you do get it back, that's terrible, the most frightening thing in the world. I know, because I've been through it.

The trouble was, we were a young side, and with a young side, everything's fine when it's going well, but when things start to go against you, it's very hard to stop the slide. It was like Billy Wallis once said, 'The trouble with a young team, it ain't got no resources.'

Our opening game was down at Southampton, who aren't a great team, but they're very difficult to play against. For one thing they're hard, very physical, for the other they've got big Ron Davies at centre-forward, winning nearly everything in the air, and not just laying it off, like Wyn Davies, but heading it for goal, as well.

He scored in the first couple of minutes; a long cross from the right, he got up to it very well, and he headed it past me high into my right-hand corner. Ray McGraw, our centre-half, turned round and shouted at me, 'Why the hell didn't you come off your line?' and I admit I did my nut, I yelled at him, 'It was your ball, you burke!' Then Jackie Noakes had a go at both of us for not calling, and altogether it was a right old carry-on in our goal area. By this time, I wasn't afraid to have a go at the defence if I thought they'd let me down, and I certainly wasn't going to take it from Ray over *that* one.

But when we got in the dressing-room, the Boss started

155

on me as well, he said, 'What did you stay on your line for, Ronnie?'

I said, 'I've got a defence in front of me, haven't I, Boss? I'm entitled to expect them to deal with crosses that far out.'

'Not when Ron Davies is there you're not,' he said. 'I told you you'd have to take risks when you saw a cross was on for him.'

Little Billy Wallis chipped in, then, very quiet, he said, 'I don't think Ronnie had much chance with it, Boss,' and the Boss turned on him, he said, '*You* think, *you* think! Well *I* think that even if he'd challenged for the ball and hadn't got it, he'd have made Ron Davies head too high; whatever *you* think,' and I felt very sorry for Billy, he just shut up and looked choked. When the Boss was in this mood, there was no crossing him. I didn't say anything, either; there was no point, though inside I was boiling. I reckoned he was being dead unfair.

Maybe it was because I went back on the field all upset that I *did* make a mistake after just a few minutes, and gave away a jammy goal.

It was another high cross, this time from the left. It was one of those fifty-fifty ones. I could have stayed, I could have gone, but naturally after all the Boss had said, I decided that I'd go for it. As soon as I'd jumped, I realized I was going to be in trouble, because Ron Davies was coming up with me like a lift. We reached the ball just about together, his head, my fists, and it went up in the air like it was in a water jet. There was nothing I could do but pray, I'd lost sight of it completely, it was somewhere behind me. I heard a thump, somebody kicking it, than another thump, and as I spun round, I saw one of their forwards putting it in the goal. Apparently what had happened was Mike Channon had his shot blocked by Ray, then put away the rebound.

Ray said, 'Don't tell me *that* was my fault!'

I said, 'No. That one wasn't.'

Bob Cullen got one back that Danny made for him, but we still lost. In the dressing-room, the Boss gave me a right rollicking; he said, 'You played like a junior! You played like it was your first game in the team! The time you should have come out, you stay on your line, the time you should have stayed on your line, you come out!'

It was so unfair, I was near crying. I said, 'But you told me to come out, Boss.'

'Yes,' he says, 'for balls like that one in the first half; not for balls you've got no chance of getting! You're getting big-headed, that's your trouble! One season in the first team, a tour with the Under 23s, and you think you know the lot, you've nothing to learn. Well, *I'll* tell you something; you've everything to learn! And if you play like that, I'll tell you where you can go back and learn it; the Reserves!'

I sat there with my head in my hands, I could hardly believe it. Even when the Boss had gone, I still sat there. Billy Wallis came up to me and said, 'Don't take it to heart, son. He does his nut like that, Charlie. By Monday, he'll have forgotten it.' But I shook my head, because whether or not he'd forgotten it, I knew I wouldn't. What he'd said was diabolical, because if the second goal was my fault, I still knew that the first one wasn't, and even if they both had been, there was no call to speak to me like that. You can make a mistake without being big-headed.

On the train back I didn't eat, I wasn't hungry. I think the Boss knew he'd gone too far, because he looked into the carriage where I was sitting on my own and said, 'It's okay, Ronnie, you're still allowed to eat with us.' I didn't answer.

Monday, down at Snaresbrook, he was quite friendly, he was saying things like, 'You know what they did in the war, Ronnie, when a pilot crashed? They put him in another aeroplane and sent him up again. That's what I'm going to do with you. Wednesday night, you'll play against the Arsenal,' which was the home game we'd got.

To me, this was a load of old rubbish, because I hadn't crashed, I'd just given away one bad goal, but being young, brooding on it, and having him go on at me like this made me start to wonder; maybe I was playing worse than I thought, maybe he was seeing things I couldn't. In the end I asked Billy Wallis, I said, 'Billy, tell me, straight up. Did I play that bad on Saturday?'

He said, 'Well, I've seen you play better, Ronnie. I think you were at fault with that second goal, but you weren't *bad*, no.'

'Thanks,' I said, '*I* didn't think I was bad.'

But I was bad on the Wednesday, no doubt of it. I know what began it, too; I was trying too hard. That was why I gave away that first goal, and that was why I got injured.

We began fairly well. They're a big, strong side, but they're not that inventive, except for Charlie George. If you can counter them in the air, where they've got these two tall fellows, Kennedy and Radford, then you're always in with a chance. Our trouble was, in games like these, that Jackie Noakes was always struggling a bit, through being small. When there was just one big fellow, like Wyn Davies, Ray McGraw could take him, but he obviously couldn't take both of them.

Naturally Arsenal tried to exploit this, pumping a lot of long balls in. Kennedy got up to one of them, early on, but Jackie challenged him, and he headed it well over. On another, Radford nodded it across to Kennedy, but this time he couldn't get much power behind his header, and I took it.

I threw it out long to Jesse Maude, who'd come back on the left; he went away and did a one-two with Danny, squared it fast and low across the edge of the box. Bob Cullen jumped over it, and Tommy Dougall hit it past Bob Wilson.

That put a bit of confidence into us and we started playing well. We made two or three chances. Wilson made a great save from a header by Danny, Bob McNab headed out a shot by Jesse that had beaten him and was on its way in – then suddenly they came away and equalized.

Charlie George brought down a high ball with two of our blokes up his back, turned on it beautifully, and sent little George Armstrong away. Armstrong crossed, I thought it was my ball, suddenly changed my mind when I saw Ray shaping for it, so when John Radford got up and beat him to it, I was left there standing like a lemon; the ball just dropped over my head and into the net. At that moment, I think I'd rather have been anywhere than where I was, with my own team in front of me, the Borough crowd behind me; in a burning house, in a sinking ship, anywhere.

Arthur Prescott walked past me, into the net, saying, 'Have I got to get this one out for you, as well?' Jackie Noakes was yelling something at me, but I deliberately shut my ears to it which wasn't difficult, the noise the crowd were making; I just saw his mouth opening and closing like a big fish.

I was determined to make up for that if I could, and the result was what often happens in a case like this, you get reckless, which for a goalkeeper is as bad as being chicken. We went on hammering away at their defence, and the next time they broke, John Radford chased after a through ball, down the middle. He'd got Ray McGraw with him, forcing him out to the right, and if I'd stayed on my goal and cut out the angle, I'd probably have taken it easy. But I was still so wild about the goal I'd given away that I came belting out of my goal and threw myself at him and the ball. Maybe at the back of my mind I was after revenge, as well, because it was Radford that had scored it.

I got the ball all right, but his boot got to me, right on the head, a pure accident, but that didn't make any difference. It was like someone let off a firework in my head, then I went out cold. Don Collins brought me round, he said, 'What did they train *you* as, then, a Japanese suicide pilot?' For a moment or two everything was fuzzy, all the colours were out of focus, the blues, the reds, the green of the grass. Then gradually, like someone had adjusted the camera, it came back sharp. I had a hell of a pain in my head, I was still a bit vague about what had happened, but when Don asked, 'Can you go on? Can you see my finger?' waving it in front of me, I said, 'Yes.'

The rest of that game I played pretty well from memory. People told me about it afterwards, saves I'd made, saves I hadn't made, another goal that I let through, from George Graham – we apparently got one, by Jesse Maude – but I didn't know a thing about it all. The Doc had a look at me in the dressing-room; he turned to Charlie Macintosh and said, 'Slight concussion,' then back to me and he said, 'But most goalkeepers are a bit dizzy, anyway, aren't they, Ronnie?' He was a great one for jokes, the old Doc.

My old man was there at the game, and of course he was terribly upset, waiting outside in the hallway afterwards, asking was I all right, wanting to take me home. At first I wasn't keen, but at that moment the Doc came out and said, 'Best thing you could do, Ronnie. Take him home at once, Mr Blake, and tie him to the bed. And, Ronnie; don't you dare drive that car.'

Well, Dad couldn't drive it either, so the end of it was we took a taxi back, and although I was still feeling pretty rough, I couldn't help noticing how uncomfortable Dad looked – I honestly think it was the first taxi he'd ever been in – wriggling about and staring out of the window like he'd got no business to be there, and any minute someone might turn up and kick him out.

When we got home Mum was in a terrible flap, she'd been rung up by people who'd been at the match, and I don't know what she expected to see. She put me straight to bed, quite honestly I was just as pleased to be there; the Doc had given me some pills. I took those, and I slept.

When I woke up on the Sunday morning I felt a lot better, and I must say I was glad to be at home. Quite a few of the lads rang up, the Boss as well, and the Doc actually came round late in the morning. 'How are you?' he says. 'Better? I was afraid you would be. Moral? Boxers don't lead with their chins, goalkeepers shouldn't lead with their heads; even when it's as thick as yours. No headache? Fine. Don't go training tomorrow. Come down to Borough and see me on Tuesday afternoon.'

Saturday I was all right again, I played. Or rather, when I say I was all right, I *felt* all right, my head was all right, but not the way I was playing. Like I said, when your confidence goes, everything goes, because at this level of football, there isn't a lot in it, there isn't much – only a split second – between a good goalkeeper and a bad one. And when your bottle goes, even if it only goes a little, you're holding off, you're pulling back, and that costs you time, as well. It's all time, goalkeeping is.

We were playing away to Manchester United, which is never an easy game, even when they aren't throwing things at you from the Stretford Road end. You've got Bobby Charlton always liable to bang them with either foot, Georgie Best doing things you can never bargain for until he's done them, when it may be too late, and Brian Kidd, who's very big and strong and goes in on everything.

In fact it was on Brian Kidd that I came unstuck. It was quite late in the game and we were 1–1. Tommy Dougall had put us ahead when Bob headed a corner back to him. Bobby Charlton had equalized with a left-footer from the edge of the box that I never even saw; I don't think any keeper could have stopped it, not Gordon Banks, not anybody. Then in the second half there was this bouncing ball – the ground was still quite hard – that Ray McGraw and Brian Kidd were chasing. I reckoned that Ray would probably get a touch and head it back to me, but the bounce took it ahead of both of them, and obviously it was going to be mine. Brian Kidd saw it, too; he suddenly accelerated, and it took me by surprise. He came in very, very fast. I put my hands to take the ball, but he just got a touch to it before I did, we both went down in a heap, and it rolled on into the net. I felt sick, I can tell you.

I knew what the Boss would say, and he did; how it was my ball, I'd had half an hour to get it, and I would have got it if I'd been keeping my eye on it, instead of the man – which I suppose was true. He said, 'A goalkeeper that pulls out of a situation like that has no right to be playing football.' I hated him, then. I didn't say anything, just stripped and got into the bath, but at that moment I never wanted to play for him again.

The next week, I was dropped; the first time ever. I didn't even hear it from him, either; I read it in the paper. I bought an *Evening Standard* in town, and there it was, 'Borough may rest their 18 year-old England Under 23 goalkeeper, Ronnie Blake, and bring back former first team keeper Terry Morgan. Said manager Charlie Macintosh, "Ronnie's had bad luck with injuries recently. He's been playing regularly in the first team since he was seventeen, and it's a great strain for a young keeper. The time may have come to take the pressure off."'

Well, that was a right old load of codswallop, but what made it worse was to find out in such a roundabout way. The next morning when I got into the Stadium – it was Friday – sure enough there was Terry Morgan's name on the team sheet. Mine wasn't anywhere, not even in the Reserves.

I may have been a bit hasty about it, I went straight on up to the Boss's office. He was sitting behind his desk; he looked up at me, not friendly, and he said, 'What do you want?'

I said, 'I want a transfer.'

He said, 'Don't be so damn stupid. You're no' getting a transfer. Your contract's got two more years to run, and

162

we've a four-year option after that. As long as I'm here, you stay here.'

I was really upset. I was choked. I said, 'If you've got no confidence in me, what's the point of keeping me?' He said, 'Who said I've got no confidence in you? You've got no confidence in yourself, that's the trouble. You gave away that goal on Saturday because you swallowed it. You know it. I know it. I want to give you the chance to get your morale back. Until you get it back, you're no use to anybody. You're only going to get hurt again.'

There was a bit of a silence, then; I looked at him, he looked at me; there didn't seem anything to say. In a way I knew he was right, but I still felt very bitter. He didn't have to say it like he had. In the end it was him who spoke; he said, 'You can have a rest this week; that's why I've not picked you for the Combination side. If you want to watch the League match, you can watch it. If you want to go away, you can go away. I'll see you on Monday, at Snaresbrook.' As I went out, he said, 'And don't go talking to the Press.'

In fact I did talk to the Press, but it was off the record and naturally I was careful who it was; by now I knew who you could trust and who you couldn't. The little local paper bloke had always been nice, always sympathetic, right from the first, and when he rang me up, I told him straight, 'I'm choked about it, but I don't want to say nothing. I realize I haven't been playing well, but I think I ought to be given a chance to play myself back again.' He said he understood and he wouldn't quote me and I knew he wouldn't.

The phone went ring, ring, ring all evening at my digs, until in the end I got Bob to answer it and say I wasn't there. But later on, about half past nine, the doorbell went, and it was Bert Gray and Lew Prentice, two of the reporters that I liked; they went nearly everywhere together. Lew came in with his hand up; like a copper. He said, 'Right! Just a few routine questions! Just a security

163

check! Nothing you say can be taken down and used in evidence against you!'

Bert said, 'Or against Charlie Macintosh,' and Lew said, 'Well; maybe Charlie Macintosh.'

Then the four of us sat there talking, drinking coffee, till near one o'clock in the morning, except when both of them borrowed the phone to put over stories, which I heard. I wasn't quoted; they just used what I'd been telling them to make it accurate, which was a change, with newspapers.

Bert said, 'The word's round that you asked for a transfer.'

I said, 'Well, maybe I did and maybe I didn't.' He said, 'I know you did, because Charlie said you didn't!'

Bob said, 'You sound as if you don't like him,' and Bert told him, 'I hate the so-and-so.'

That was an eye-opener to me, because I'd always reckoned that the Press liked him, the stories he kept giving them, the quotes, the booze he handed out after every home game. But then we heard it all. Bert said, 'He's a liar. When he dies, they'll have to screw him into the ground,' and we started hearing all about the things they said he'd told them that weren't true, what he used to get up to on tour when he was a player, how he was always looking for lolly. Bert said, 'At Wolves, they used to call him What's-in-it-for-Me Macintosh.'

In a way I was glad to hear all this, but Bob Cullen was sort of embarrassed, I could see it. Like most of us, he'd looked up to the Boss, and nothing had happened to change it – yet. In the end I asked the two of them, 'What do you think I ought to do?'

Bert said, 'Stay. You'll be there longer than he is, anyway.' I didn't ask him what he meant.

Going back in the Reserves was terrible, like being dropped into a cold bath. Most of the old faces were gone, the ones you'd left behind, which was something, but you still had people giving you the odd look, and as for the atmosphere, it was miserable, after what you'd got used to, like a cemetery, hardly anybody on the terraces, no tension, nothing to put you on your toes; in fact everything to remind you you'd been slung out, shoved into a backwater where nothing that happened mattered. You could play the best game in the world, and all it would get you was five lines in the local paper. I was properly depressed, I can tell you.

There were times, I admit it, when I thought this was the end of the road, that I'd never get back my form, never get back in the team.

First of all there was quite a bit of publicity, me being dropped after coming through so quick. I was on the telly; one of the papers even sent a bird round to interview me, a nice little dolly with big, saucer eyes she kept turning on you, but it wasn't much consolation, being written about because you'd been dropped. I said when she left, 'Come back and see me when I'm picked for England,' which of course I didn't mean seriously, just sarcastically, but it was silly of me, because wouldn't you know she went and used it. In the paper, it looked terrible.

The worst thing about it was that when you're dropped, a sort of barrier seems to come down between you and your mates. You're just as friendly with them, and that, it's not like anybody stops speaking to you, it's just that you're in different Leagues, they're off doing one thing, the thing that matters, preparing for it all the week, and you're doing something nobody's bothered about. My money went down, naturally, no crowd bonuses, nothing for League position (not that anyone was getting much, then) though the basic stayed all right, but this wasn't what worried me.

Even between me and Bob Cullen, living in the same house, facing each other across the dining-room table maybe two or three times a day, you felt the barrier there. It's not that Bob said anything, it's not that I did, in fact it was more what he didn't say, because he's a nice bloke, he'd

never mention what was happening in the first team games
unless I brought it up; which naturally I often did. Then,
being polite, he'd ask, 'How did *you* get on?' and I
wouldn't want to tell him, 'Beat Charlton Reserves,' or
'Drew with Orient Reserves.' Big stuff.

Dad was great about it, as always, you could rely on him
to see the bright side of anything. His theory was, I'd been
lucky. He said, 'A goalkeeper comes in as young as you did,
there's got to be some kind of a reaction, it don't matter
how brilliant he is. And you're lucky that it's happened
now, when the team's playing bad, because in my opinion,
you're well out of it. Later on, they'll turn the corner, and
it'll be easier to come back.'

I told him, 'I don't know about *them* playing bad, I know
I was playing bad,' but he said, 'If a team ain't playing well,
a goalkeeper can't play well, Not indefinitely. A goalkeeper's only human; especially *your* age.'

One game, down at Millwall, The Den, playing their reserves, I went behind the goal to collect the ball for a goal
kick, someone called to me. I looked up, and there was
Mike. Smiling. That was all I needed, I thought, and when I
took the goalkick, I sliced it, it went straight into touch on
our half of the field. But a few minutes later when I made a
save, turned one over the bar that was going into the top
corner, I heard him shouting, 'That's it, Ronnie, that's a bit
of the old style,' and for some reason, I felt very pleased.
After the game, I wondered would he be there, but he
wasn't, and I thought what a hell of a long way it was to
cycle, all the way from Notting Hill, over to south-east
London.

He turned up again for one or two of the matches, and it
got to where I'd look for him when I ran into goal, for the
kick-about. He'd wave and smile, it was almost like he was
pleased I was in the Reserves again, because now he could
get near me. He was a funny fellow, Mike.

And to tell the truth, I think it was doing me a bit of

good. Everything being slower, it made things a lot easier. The movements weren't as quick, the shots weren't made as quick, they didn't challenge you so hard on the high balls. For the first game or two, I was making mistakes, even there, but after a little while, I felt it coming back again. I'd throw myself at someone's feet and come out holding the ball, or I'd get up to a high one and hold that, too, and I'd think to myself, that's it, it won't be long, now.

As for the first team, they were having a terrible time. The first match I was out, they went up to Newcastle and got beaten five, in midweek, then they played at home to Chelsea on the Saturday, and lost, 1–0. Naturally I asked Bob Cullen how Terry Morgan had played, and he'd shrug and say, 'Not bad, not good.' I'd ask, 'Could he have stopped them?' really meaning, of course, would *I* have stopped them, even though the reason I was out was that I hadn't been stopping them, and after Newcastle, Bob said, 'Well, maybe the last two, but by then we'd all more or less chucked it in.'

A couple of weeks later, Bob was in the Reserves himself. It happened after we'd drawn at home 2–2 with Liverpool; he came home that night and he was practically in tears, he said, 'The things he said to me, the things he called me. All right, I missed a couple of chances, but why put it all down to me?' Being upset, he'd said a few things directly after the game, too, to some reporters, and one of them was a news agency bloke that put it in one of the papers, so there it was, the Sunday morning: CULLEN SLAMS MANAGER MACINTOSH and the rest of it.

On the Monday, the Boss gave him a rollicking, fined him a hundred quid, which was a hell of a lot of money to anybody, and told him he was dropped to the Reserves. Naturally I was very, very sorry for Bob, he was shattered, though from my own point of view, I admit it was nice to have a mate playing with me. Someone you could have a moan with, and talk about the game to, when you got home, even if the game didn't matter. Bob did what I did, he asked for a transfer, and the Boss refused; he was told the same as me, that his contract still had years to run, and even after that, the club had an option. Bob said, 'I reckon they're one way, these contracts, all for the club and nothing for the player,' and Tommy Dougall, who was listening said, 'Have you only just worked that out?'

'Well,' I said, because Tommy got a little on my wick at times, 'if you're so dead clever, Tommy, I suppose you got a different contract from the rest of us?' He said, 'There's *no* different contract. We're all peasants, the lot of us, however much we earn,' which *I* couldn't see.

Another time, Tommy suddenly asked me, 'What'll you do when you're finished playing?' and I looked at him like he was daft. 'Me?' I said. 'Do me a favour,' I said, 'I'm only nineteen.'

'Yes,' he said, 'but one day you'll be twenty, that's not long, then you'll be twenty-five, then thirty, then thirty-five. Even a goalkeeper doesn't go on forever.'

'Well,' I said, 'we'll see when it comes, won't we?' Because to me, though I knew it would have to come some day, this was just something you had in the back of your mind somewhere, it was too far off to be real. I said, 'What'll *you* do, anyway? Be a manager?'

'No!' he said. 'Not *me*! A manager! Have you taken a look at directors? Even *our* directors; and they're meant to be about the best ones. Dead ignorant about the game. Boozing and swilling. No, no. I'll finish in the gutter.'

I looked at him; it was sometimes hard to know if he was being serious.

In fact, he was the next one to be slung out, the next one to be in the Reserves, after the first team had lost 1–0 at Derby. He played a couple of games for us, dribbling himself into trouble time after time, beating three or four men and losing it to the fourth or fifth, then he went back into the first team. Then Bob went in again, away to Ipswich, we lost that one, too, 2–1, and the next week he was back with me in the Reserves.

Nobody knew where they were, it was terrible; it was becoming a joke. One morning, down at Snaresbrook, little Billy Wallis was going about looking very depressed. Someone in the dressing-room asked him what was the matter, and he said, 'I've been sacked.' Well, we couldn't believe it, we were all of us shattered. Everyone liked Bill; in a quiet sort of way, he'd helped everybody, and although he might not have been very forceful, most of us reckoned that one forceful character in the club was enough. Besides, that was another reason why we'd never thought he'd go, because he never gave Charlie Macintosh an argument.

He said, 'Charlie told me this morning. I still can't really take it in. Didn't give no reasons. Just said, "It's no use, Billy, I like you, but you've got to go. If you like, you can leave tomorrow." I don't know how I'll break it at home.'

The next week, we got a new coach, Jack Sale, who'd been managing Accrington. He'd been the England centre-half not all that long ago, a big, dark bloke, losing his hair, very quiet; I must say I liked him. The Boss gave him more say in the training than Billy had had, he started spending less time himself down at Snaresbrook, leaving it to Jack and Don Collins, and the atmosphere got a little better. The results didn't get much better, though, and the next bomb-shell was when Bob Cullen got sold.

It happened the way Billy Wallis had been sacked, just like that. One Friday morning the Boss called him in and said, 'Blackpool have made a bid for you. If I was you, I'd go; there's no future for you here.' So what could poor old Bob do but go? He was in a terrible state that night, crying, saying he felt like giving up the game, wondering how he could ever settle down in the North. But the next week, he went up to Blackpool, met their manager, Bob Stokoe, who he said was a right nice bloke, and the end of it was, he signed.

Or rather, it wasn't the end of it. About a fortnight later, as it turned out, Blackpool were at home to Borough. Bob played, he had a blinder, and he scored the winning goal. I'm told when he did, he looked up into the stand, where he knew the Boss would be, and made a sign at him. It didn't sound like Bob to me, as I knew him, but after what he'd been through, I didn't blame him. Jesse Maude moved in with me, in his place.

By this time, we were one from bottom of the First Division, and the team were playing terribly. The Boss had put Danny centre-forward, where he was taking a lot of stick. As for Terry Morgan, I heard he wasn't doing too well, but the way things were, I was quite pleased to be in the stiffs.

When I came back, it was the last game I'd have chosen. Though we were doing so badly in the League, our coming third the last season meant we were in this European Union Cup, that had been the Fairs Cup. We'd had an easy draw in the first round, some little Norwegian team that even we couldn't help beating, then we were drawn against a Greek side, in Athens.

None of the lads fancied that a lot, especially with the first leg out there, because from what we'd heard, it was like a boxer going to fight in some of these European countries; you had to knock them out to get a draw. Jack Sale went out to have a look at them; he came back and he said, '*They*'re hard, the ground's hard, and the crowd are animals.'

I reckoned I was well out of it, especially the way the first team was still playing, but the Saturday before, playing up at Everton, Terry Morgan got a kick on the thigh, and had to pull out. On the Monday, down at Snaresbrook, the Boss told me I was in. He said, 'This is a great chance to re-establish yourself. We're going in for a draw, so you're going to have plenty to do, though most of it'll probably be high, bouncing stuff. Play well for me out there, and *I'll* look after *you*.'

But it wasn't the same any more, if I wanted to play well now, it was for me, not for him, or at any rate, just for the team. Normally I'd have been quite interested, going to a country like Greece, that I'd never seen, but this time I could have done without it. There was a terrible atmosphere in the team, everybody moaning, a few still backing up the Boss, the players he was favouring – Danny was one of them – the rest just cheesed off.

Still, at least when we got there the sun was shining, and there seemed to be things happening. The Greeks looked after us so well, you'd have thought we were there to play a friendly. They took us round the town, we went up this hill with the ruined temple, which looked fabulous, and Danny told me he'd been chatting with the interpreter, who'd said he'd show us around a bit, that evening. I wasn't too sure about that, because we'd got the game the next day, but Danny said, 'That's okay, we'll just have a scout round, we'll get back early to the hotel, then maybe we'll line something up for after the banquet, tomorrow night.' Tommy Dougall said he'd come, too. Ray McGraw was another, and we fixed up to meet this bloke after supper.

The ground we had to play on was terrible, specially for a goalkeeper. Not a blade of grass, the ball bouncing diabolically. Even if I wore knee pads and elbow pads, I knew I'd have no skin left, by the time the game was finished.

That night, the interpreter came round like he'd promised, he was a nice little bloke, spoke very good English, he'd been in the Greek navy, and we all went off together; we told Jack Sale we were going for a walk.

He took us down a lot of funny little narrow streets till we got to what he called a café, though to me it was more of a drinking place, blokes strumming away and singing, hardly any birds, now and then a few of the men getting up and doing a dance, all arm-in-arm, which was a bit of a

171

giggle. George, the interpreter, ordered some wine, this *ouzo*, yellow stuff, very dry; I tasted a little and I didn't like it, but the other three seemed to like it all right. In fact they liked it a bit too much.

It all got very cheerful before long. George told some of the people round us who we were, and they started toasting us, telling us they liked England, but they hoped we'd lose, and we told them we liked Greece, but we hoped *they*'d lose. The end of it was we found ourselves dancing too, arm-in-arm, with a lot of Greeks, wandering about all over the floor; I must say I enjoyed it. But suddenly, when I started wondering what the time was, it was after midnight. George laughed, he said, 'But you are not Cinderella, I think!' I said, 'We'll be turned into a ruddy pumpkin all right if the Boss catches us.'

But the others didn't care, they were well away. Tommy poured himself another drink and said, 'So-and-so the Boss. The Boss can jump in the lake,' and George said, 'You mean in the Aegean.' Tommy said, 'I don't care where it is, as long as he jumps.'

I wanted to go back, but I couldn't on my own, and anyway, it wasn't on to leave them in it. By the time we did get back, it was after one o'clock. There was no one in the hotel entrance hall, just the porter, nobody waiting in our rooms – I was sharing with Danny. The next morning we slept in late, like we always do. I woke up feeling okay, but Danny was still flat out. I must say I didn't fancy going downstairs. I had some breakfast sent up, had a bath and, when there was a knock on the door, I jumped six feet into the air. But it wasn't the Boss, it was only Ray McGraw.

He said, 'The Boss knows.' I said, 'I reckoned he would.' He said, 'Jack told me he knows. But he's no' speaking to me. He walked right past me. I reckon he'll maybe save it till after the game, so if we win it, we could be okay.' Then he made a face and put his hand to his head, he said, 'Gee, I wish I didn't have to head the ball.'

'You're all right,' I said, 'at least you don't have to dive for it.'

At the team talk, the Boss still didn't say a word about it, but I noticed that he didn't talk direct to any of the four of us. Tommy and Danny looked worse than Ray, in fact I'd had to wake Danny up in the end and put him under a cold shower. All he could say was, 'The Greek so-and-so, the Greek so-and-so.' He reckoned it had all been a plot.

If it was, then it worked pretty well, because that night we got hammered. The refereeing didn't help. They were a hard team, and they came in from the very beginning and hit us with everything; obstruction, shirt-pulling, kicking, the lot. The ref was a little Austrian. He never stopped blowing, but whenever he did, it was nearly always for them, not for us. He was penalizing us for everything, every tackle, he even threatened to send Graham Gibbs off for a tackle from behind, it was unbelievable. He was obviously scared stiff of the crowd, and mind you, I didn't blame him. The noise they were making, right from the very beginning, the way they were carrying on, I was very pleased they'd got this wire fence round the pitch, though as you'll see, it still wasn't enough.

The first corner they got, a bloke held me down, he hung on to my jersey, and I only shook myself free after I'd given him the elbow. He lay there on the ground with his hands over his face, rolling about, and the crowd went mad. I was worried, I can tell you. A couple of their players made for me, but the lads kept them back, in the end, it cooled down.

Not for long, though. The next thing that happened was that Danny flicked a ball over the head of their centre-half and was running round him when the bloke just took a swinging kick at him, waist high, and brought him down. Tommy Dougall just did his nut, he got hold of the fellow by his jersey, a couple more Greeks weighed in and started kicking Tommy, and the next thing you knew, there was about twenty supporters over the wall and the police were heading towards the punch-up from all over the field.

I didn't know what to do, join in or stay where I was; I started out towards it, but Jack Sale ran on to the field from the trainer's bench and pulled me back, he said, 'Stay out of it, Ronnie.'

Anyway, the coppers whacked a few people with their truncheons, both trainers came on, and after about ten minutes, we went on with the game; if you could call it that. By this time, Danny was limping about, and Tommy Dougall and Ray McGraw were obviously feeling what had happened last night. In fact they got their first goal when Ray missed his header, and their centre-forward said thank you very much and headed in.

The Boss pulled Danny off and put on Ernie Leech, who was a substitute, but it didn't make much odds. We still gave away another goal before half-time, and it was partly my fault. When you've been in reserve football that long, your reflexes go a bit, you can't help it, and this was the last game I'd ever have chosen to come back in.

Their centre-forward, who could play a bit on the ground, lost Ray McGraw, and shot. I got to it all right, it was going quite low for the left-hand corner, but it was a light ball and I couldn't hold it; it bounced off my chest, hit Jackie Noakes, who was belting back, and went into the net.

In the dressing-room, the Boss called us every name under the sun, and quite a few I'd never heard. He pulled off Ray and put on Arthur Jones, a big boy who'd just joined us from Stockport; he told me that if there'd been an experienced goalkeeper on the bench, he'd have pulled me off, too; there was only Gerry Godfrey, the youth keeper. He said, 'And don't think I don't know why some of you are playing the way you are; we'll talk about *that* afterwards.' It was a nice frame of mind to go back on the field in, and I wonder we didn't let in a few more.

Arthur Jones was struggling, you couldn't really blame him. They were still kicking at everything that moved in defence, the few times we looked like doing anything. They hit the bar once, I made a couple of reflex saves I didn't know that much about, from shots close in, and the end of it was we were quite happy losing only 2–0, which at least gave us a chance in the return. Jackie Noakes was saying in the dressing-room, 'Wait till we get those so-and-sos at Borough, wait till we get them at home.'

Back in the hotel, the Boss sent for Tommy, Ray, Danny and me. After he'd given us a proper rollicking for what we'd done the night before, he said, 'The four of you are suspended for three weeks, you're fined a hundred and fifty pounds – and your all on the transfer list.'

That was what staggered me; not the first two things, because I'd expected those, but being on the list; I couldn't believe it. He said, 'I've no use for disloyal players, however talented they are. I'll take a player with more heart and less talent, any time.'

When we came out of his room, Ray sort of shrugged it off. Tommy said he was pleased, he said, 'Who wants to play for him, anyway, the hooligan?' but Danny and I were walking around in a daze. What would happen? Where would we go? London had been my whole life, and now here I was, I might be transferred to Newcastle or Liverpool or Sheffield or somewhere, I'd have to start a whole new life. To me, even when I'd been dropped to the Reserves, Borough was still my club, the one I wanted to stay with.

Danny said, 'He can't make us go,' which of course was true; we could always say no. But knowing the Boss a bit better now, you couldn't help realizing he could make it quite nasty for you.

What I don't think anybody realized, including the Boss, was the stink it would all make. When we got back to London airport, there were television cameras waiting, dozens of photographers, the lot. I don't think I've ever seen the Boss so taken aback. Usually he was very easy with reporters, making jokes, making them laugh, but with this lot he was quite stroppy, and he turned to us and said, 'No interviews! Nobody says a word!'

When I got back to my digs, our landlady told me the phone had never stopped going. In the end she'd had to take it off, and Jesse and I told her, 'You can leave it off.' I didn't want to talk to anybody, except Dad and Mum. I knew they'd be worried, so I rang them right away. The old man was really upset, he said, 'What did you do it for? Mum said the moment she heard about it, "That's not like our Ronnie. He must have been led astray."' And I could just hear her saying it.

I told him, 'I didn't even have a drink, Dad, I was just out late, that's all.'

He said, 'That's still not right, is it, not when you've got a match to play the next day, an important one,' and what could I tell him? I knew the way he thought; the thing that frightened him was maybe I'd lose my job, because for Dad, that was the worst thing in the world, whereas for me, though obviously I was fed up losing all that money, the big thing was not wanting to leave London, not wanting all this upheaval; the having to start all over again. But as for getting another club, well, obviously I'd get one, even though it mightn't be the one I wanted. I mean, after all, there were ninety-two League clubs, which was what I said to him. But it didn't do any good.

Being suspended meant we weren't even allowed to train, which to me was just ridiculous; it meant that when he wanted us again, we wouldn't be fit. Filling in the day was hard, when you were used to a routine. I went to the pictures quite a bit, watched the telly, took a few birds out dancing in the evenings, went to the dogs once with Danny, over at White City. But it was difficult. Now and again a reporter would ring and say, 'I hear so and so are interested in you.' I heard Leeds and West Ham, which would have suited me, and Burnley, but nothing came of it.

A week after it had all happened, Ray McGraw got transferred to Aston Villa. Jesse Maude said, 'We're dropping like flies.' He was lucky, Jesse; nothing much worried him. Now and again I went home, but not too often because, like I said, they were all upset about it, and it would get me down. Terry Morgan went back in the side, but by now the spirit just wasn't there. They went down again at Manchester City, then when the return with the Greeks came round, I was in two minds whether to go or not; I was still barred from the ground, it would have meant I'd have to pay. I asked Danny was he going, and he said, 'You're joking!' and in the end I decided that I'd stay away myself, because I just couldn't face the remarks, if I went in the crowd.

So I listened to it on the radio. I started off half wanting them to lose, I admit, but as the game went on, I got properly caught up in it, till I was standing up and shouting; the landlady came in to ask was anything the matter. The Greeks did what you'd have expected them to do, played with nine men in defence and sometimes ten, and the worst of it was they got a jammy early goal. They broke out of their half, their right-winger put across a centre, it hit Joe Lyons, bounced back to another of their forwards, and he scored.

After that it was all Borough, but without Danny and Tommy, what could you expect? Jesse got one, near half-time, the equalizer, but that was it; we were knocked out on aggregate. I felt very, very depressed. I suppose that what I'd secretly been hoping was we'd get through, then I could come back in the later rounds.

Those three weeks were about the longest in my life. Danny said we ought to take off for Majorca, make the most of it, but I just couldn't do that, I felt too unsettled, I wanted to know what was going on.

The next one to go was Tommy Dougall; Manchester United paid a hundred thousand pounds for him. I couldn't believe it, I couldn't understand how Borough could let a player like Tommy go, because with all his faults he was still brilliant, he could still do things for you that no one else could. Danny rang me up and said, 'If I wasn't on the list already, I'd *ask* to go on. It's going to be nice playing centre-forward up there, all on your own with three people kicking you and no one giving you the ball.' But by the time the three weeks were up, Danny and I were still there.

At training, the Boss was quite friendly; you never knew where you were with him, now. The one he seemed to have it in for at the moment was Graham Gibbs, which amazed me, because Graham was like Jesse in this; never any trouble, always a hundred per cent, give you everything. But for the Boss, nothing he could do was right, and I could see it was getting him down. Normally he was very cheerful, but now he looked drawn, he looked miserable. The Boss would say things like, 'Always the same when a player gets married,' which Graham just had done. 'Takes a whole season to adjust. If I had my way, I'd forbid my players to marry!' He said it like it was a joke, but Danny said, 'I bet he would, and all.'

That Saturday, we were both in the Reserves, up at Ipswich. Danny was just strolling about, not bothering, but a couple of times he did turn it on; he went past three men in the first half, hit it, and their keeper made a good save. Then in the second half he climbed up beautifully to a cross from the left, and headed a goal; the only one of the game – and made a great thing out of dancing about, waving his fist at the crowd, what there was of it. Some of them shouted, 'Big head,' not realizing he was taking the mickey.

A week or so later the Boss took us both off the list; the

first we knew about it was from the papers. According to them, he was supposed to have said, 'They're just young boys, and I think they have both learned their lesson.'

Danny said to me the next day, 'What lesson's that? That it's no use playing for a burke like him? I've a good mind to go in and ask to be put on the list again. He never asked *me* if I wanted to come off.' But that was Danny. In fact all the Boss said, just casual like, was, 'You're off the list, you two,' at the end of the morning's training. It was getting harder and harder to understand him; he seemed to be upsetting everybody except the young players that he kept on bringing into the team.

Danny was back in the first team that Saturday, at Huddersfield; apparently he scored a good goal, but we still went down, 4–2. Myself, I was in the stiffs again at home to Brentford; we won 5–0 and I might as well have watched it from the terraces, for all I had to do. The next week, *I* got back, which I suppose should have meant something, but it didn't. I didn't feel glad, I didn't feel sorry. I didn't even feel nervous about would I do well, because this was the atmosphere we had in the club; we were just going through the motions.

We were at home to Derby, and once the game began, I felt the old interest coming back a bit, especially as I made an early save. Alan Hinton hit one of those twenty-five yard shots of his from out on the left; it was going like a bomb for the far, top corner, but I managed to get up to it and turn it over with my left hand. The crowd liked that, they cheered me, there was a lot of, 'Good old Ronnie!' which was just as well, because I was busy most of the game.

The defence just wasn't the same without old Ray there, and the midfield wasn't the same without Tommy. That week we'd bought a little Scottish bloke, an inside-forward called Willy Paterson, from Airdrie. He was good on the ball all right, but like most of them that come out of the

Scottish League, he needed time to adjust to the pace, and he was getting caught in possession. Two or three times Derby got away like this, and in the end they scored.

Willy Paterson lost the ball to Colin Todd, he hit a long one out to Hinton, who crossed, John O'Hare headed down, and Kevin Hector smacked it on the half volley. I'd got no chance.

In the old days, when I first got into the side, that kind of thing didn't worry us too much; we just took it in our stride and went after the equalizer. But now, the way things were, you could almost feel the spirit go out of the team. About ten minutes later, Jackie Noakes played a ridiculous ball back to me, Hector was in on it, and that was number two. I gave Jackie a proper rollicking, I can tell you, but he wouldn't have it, it was unbelievable, he was actually standing there trying to tell me it was my fault! A goalkeeper usually knows when he's at fault all right, and when this happened, it just cheesed me off completely; I thought right, if that's your attitude, I'll play for myself, not you, because a goalkeeper can. He can't always cover up a defender's mistakes, but he can sometimes make them look worse than they are.

We went in to get the usual roasting from the Boss. Now that Tommy wasn't there, nobody even argued, but I saw the new bloke, little Paterson, looking about a bit wide-eyed, like it wasn't what he'd been used to in Scotland. With a team that's in the state we were, that sort of thing doesn't do any good at all, in fact it does harm. We went out for the second half feeling worse, not better, and we gave away a third goal not long before the end, when there was a scramble round our goal, and Hector, I think it was, got a touch to it. I said to Jackie Noakes, 'Go on! Tell me it was my ruddy ball!' but he didn't say a word, just turned away from me. In his own way, he was as sick as I was.

Monday and Tuesday, the Boss didn't turn up for training. Tuesday afternoon, the phone went in our digs, I picked it up, and it was Lew Prentice. He said, 'You've heard Charlie Macintosh has resigned?'

I thought he was having me on, I said, 'You're joking.' He said, 'No, I'm not. It's just come over the wire. Contract terminated by mutual agreement, which is a complicated way of saying he's been fired. Jack Sale's taking over as acting manager.'

I yelled to Jesse Maude, who was upstairs, 'Jesse! The Boss has been fired! He's out!' and Jesse came down the stairs four at a time, he said, 'If you're kidding me, I'll kill you!'

'No,' I said, 'I'm not kidding you! It's Lew Prentice; he's just heard about it at his paper. Jack Sale's taking over!'

'Great!' he said. 'Great!'

Lew Prentice said, 'Can I quote you as saying you're glad?' I said, 'You can quote me as saying it's the best thing that could have happened to Borough.'

'I can't do that,' he said, 'it may be true, but it's libellous. I'll think of something.'

I put down the phone and Jesse and I did a little dance around the room.

It was amazing, the change in the club. People were suddenly cheerful again, the whole atmosphere was different. Everybody liked Jack Sale, because they believed in him, they knew he always stood by what he said, that if you gave him a hundred per cent, he'd always back you; and he knew the game, as well. He called us all together at Snaresbrook, the first team and the Reserves. He just said that he knew things hadn't been too good in the club, but now we were going to start again. We'd done well the last season, and we'd got the talent to do well, this. He said obviously we'd got no chance in the League, but he was sure we weren't going to be relegated, either – we were two points off the bottom, then. And if we were out of the European

Union Cup, there was still the F.A. Cup; we could have a go for that.

Which we did. In fact you saw the change immediately, that Saturday, when we went to Tottenham and won 3–1. There was a completely different spirit in the team, like a cloud had lifted, everybody running for everyone else, where before everyone had been blaming everyone else. This little Willy Paterson had a blinder; he was always finding space for himself, so you could give him the ball, and he was using it beautifully. He might not have the strength Tommy Dougall had, the ball control, but he was a lot more accurate with his passes; and he didn't hold on till everybody had been marked. Danny shook them with an early goal that he headed off a centre by Joe Lyons, who was overlapping; Jesse Maude got another, a lovely first-time shot.

In the second half, Spurs got one by Martin Peters, one of those long throws from Martin Chivers, headed on to him by Gilzean, but just near the end Graham Gibbs ran on to a loose ball that had been headed out of the area and really belted it past Jennings. We won the next three on the trot.

Then it was January, and the Cup. We were all praying not to get another Third Division team away, like Tranmere the year before, and we didn't; in fact we got a Fourth Division team at home, Hartlepools, who'd got through somehow. We did them 5–1, no trouble, then we were away to Orient, a London derby. They played well, you have to give them that, but they tired near the end, it was a very heavy pitch, and we put in a couple through Ernie Leech and Harry Jackson, who was really on form now, with Willy Paterson to play with instead of Tommy, who'd always rather confused him.

In the League, we lost a couple, but mostly we were winning at home and drawing away, we were well out of trouble by the Fifth Round of the Cup. This time we drew

Leicester at home; they're always hard to beat in the Cup. I made an early save from Rodney Fern, when Cross came up and put him right through. For a long time it looked as if they might hold us to a replay, they got very defensive near the end. Danny got the ball in the area with his back to goal, beat Sjoberg with one of those fantastic turns of his, and shot. Peter Shilton made a great save, I honestly don't know how he got to it, but Ernie Leech was following up, and put it in. I couldn't help feeling sorry for Peter, though naturally I was delighted for us.

The Sixth Round was Stoke, and we needed a replay; we drew with them 1-1 up there, then they took us to extra time at Borough. It was 1-1 at full time, again. John Ritchie headed one for them, Harry Jackson got one from outside the box for us, but soon after it restarted, Danny was brought down in the box, and Graham Gibbs scored from the penalty, though it was a dicey one, his shot went in off the bar.

The semi-finals, we were drawn against West Bromwich at Villa Park, with Everton playing Arsenal in the other one. Naturally we weren't that keen on having to meet Albion so near their own ground, it was almost a home game for them. The directors thought about protesting, but in the end they didn't, they let it go on.

Personally I was never too keen on playing against Albion, unless it was at Borough, because they weren't all that, away. But when they were on song, they had this Astle and Brown thing going, and there was always Asa Hartford, hitting these shots first time from outside the box.

There was a terrible wind at Villa that day which made things difficult, but we got away well. After about ten minutes, a move we'd planned from a free kick came off, and gave us a goal. It started off with the old dodge, two players running at the ball, Danny and Ernie, like one was going to jump over it, and the other was going to kick it. Which is what they did, except that instead of shooting when Ernie jumped over it, Danny played a diagonal ball, wide of the wall, and out to the right. It needed dead accurate timing, otherwise Ernie would have been offside, but he wasn't. He caught up with the ball on the by-line, hooked it across, and Harry Jackson came in from the left to head past the keeper.

After that, we neither of us created very much; it was mostly high crosses and long shots, but I was getting out to them well, and the only header Jeff Astle had went well over the top. Just near the end, though, he worked the old trick, he headed one back for Tony Brown, on the edge of the box. Brown hit a screamer, it was going high to my left. I hardly had time to react, I just took off and flung myself to it, praying I could get it, and I did, with the tips of my fingers; the ball cleared the bar, and I was just as glad our defence headed the corner away, because that left hand was numb. I didn't care, though. We were in the Final.

Everton beat Arsenal in the other; so we'd play them.

You never know how many friends you've got, till you're in a Cup Final. People you haven't seen since maybe you were a kid. Relatives. People that say they're relatives. People that are meant to have taught you all you knew when you were starting. I don't count Mike among those, because he *did* help me. In fact I told my parents, 'If Mike comes round, tell him I'll look after him,' and he did and they did. And *I* did.

The phone went so much at our digs that Jesse and I left it off most of the time. Some of the lads sold their tickets to the spivs and made a bit of money out of them, but with myself, by the time I'd finished giving them away, or selling them for what they'd cost to people I didn't know that well, I'd got none left.

Then there was the usual Cup Final pool, everything any of us got for interviews, photographs, advertisements and that going in, to be split up at the end. Jack Sale took us off for special training at Eastbourne, which was a superstition, really, because the last time the club had won the Cup, twenty years or so ago, that was where they'd trained. Jack had a suit he'd worn in every round, too, and a red handkerchief that he'd had in the pocket. Then there was Ernie Leech, whose car had been in dock when we played the Third Round, so he'd been given a lift by Graham Gibbs that day, which they'd kept up for all the home Cup-ties afterwards. Naturally Graham drove him to Borough on the morning of the Final, to catch the coach.

I admit it was a strain, that coach ride. We had the radio playing, some of the lads joined in the pop songs, but me, I couldn't, I was too tensed up, my stomach was in knots, even though I'd been at Wembley as a schoolboy. People are right when they say there's nothing like a Final, the atmosphere. You get in sight of Wembley, you see those old towers, you think of all the matches there's been there, the great players who've played, the goals that have been scored; and, if you're a keeper, the goals that have been given away there.

That was what was terrifying me: throwing one in. I'd even dreamed about it, and I knew there were things that had happened to goalkeepers there that were worse than a nightmare; Bert Trautmann, the German who played for Manchester City, breaking his neck; and still playing on. Another bloke, an Arsenal goalkeeper that the old man had told me about, years and years ago catching a ball then letting it slip through his arms and across the line; the only goal of the match, the winner. So naturally I went through all my own little routines, like keeping the same jersey I'd worn in every round, seeing that Jesse went out of the house before I did, getting my mother to ring me that morning because she had on the day of the Third Round, and when I got there, even rubbing a bit of chewing-gum on my hands, like Harry Vaughan. And of course I made sure I'd come out of the tunnel last but one.

There was a telly in the dressing-room, and before the match we sat there watching it, which now I think was the worst thing we could have done, because the tension just built and built; the old geezer in the white jacket on his platform, leading the singing, the whole crowd standing up for 'Abide With Me', the managers of other clubs coming on and saying who they fancied, us or Everton. Building and building.

Jack Sale just quietly ran through what he'd already told us, the things we ought to look for, like Joe Royle nodding them about in the box – he didn't need to remind *me* – and Howard Kendall coming through looking for a shot. Then at last it was time to go on, down that smelly old tunnel, side by side with Everton, into the sunlight – it was a lovely day – on to that beautiful pitch, all springy under your feet, into the tremendous noise. The Duke of Kent shook hands with both teams. He said something or other to me, but I couldn't tell you what it was, I never heard it. Some of the lads on both teams could spot people they knew, wives and relatives, in the crowd. I looked around for where I thought Mum and Dad would be, but I couldn't see them. I thought that was a bad omen.

Then at last we were away; and I got my early save all right, but not the way I wanted it. We couldn't have been playing a minute when the ball went out to Johnny Morrissey, on their left. It's a hell of a big pitch, Wembley, which is probably why Arthur Prescott was standing off him where normally he plays the winger close. Anyway, Morrissey had time to get it under control, turn on it as Arthur came in, and whip across an inswinging centre.

It was a nasty one, one of those fifty-fifty balls that you know if you get you aren't going to hold. Joe Royle and I went in for it together, I got a hand to it and pushed it out, then I went down with a hell of a bang, and couldn't get up. What happened was I think his knee had gone into my thigh; it was pure accident, but I knew it was a bad one.

186

Don Collins ran on and started massaging it; it hurt like hell, and it was a couple of minutes before I could stand up. When I did, it started throbbing, and I knew that if I ever had to dive on it, it was going to be murder, and of course, I couldn't take the goal-kicks. Jumping wasn't going to be too easy, either. I could have cried, I tell you.

Luckily we were playing well, and I didn't have that much to do. Graham, Harry, and little Willy Paterson were getting the edge on Ball, Kendall and Harvey in midfield, which was surprising, because that was where Everton had their strength. Danny had a shot and a header saved by Rankin, and the only difficult thing I had to do was go up to a cross by Tommy Wright. I was definitely handicapped, it was one I'd normally have caught, no trouble, but with Royle coming in, I didn't risk it; I punched it clear.

In the dressing-room at half-time the Doc took a look at my thigh, pressed it about a bit, and I practically jumped off the table. He said, 'You'd better have an injection. It should last you most of the half.'

Jack Sale said to me, 'Think you can do it?' I said, 'I've got to, haven't I?'

The injection worked, it took the pain away, though I was still stiff. And it was just as well I'd had it, because early in the half, little Alan Ball twirled past a couple of our defenders and put in a low one on the turn, to my left. I got down to it and held; I didn't feel anything.

We were defending the Borough end now, the goal with all our supporters behind it, and it was good to hear them all cheering, where the other end it had been, 'Everton, Everton!' the whole time. Whatever happened, I knew I couldn't let them down.

And then we scored; the best cure I could have had. It was a lovely movement, all along the ground, four or five passes, with Danny picking up in it twice. In the end he took a couple of defenders with him, making right, sud-

187

denly turned and made a reverse pass, left, and Graham Gibbs came tearing in, pulled it past Labone with his right foot, and hit it past Rankin with his left. I was dancing about on the line, thigh or no thigh.

The goal gave us even more of an edge, the way goals will, and all I had to do in the next twenty minutes or so was come out and pick up a couple of long through balls, and catch a few easy crosses, including a corner. But then it started again, the pain, far worse than before. It was like knives stabbing at me, and I knew one thing that if it came to diving on that right thigh, it was going to be like jumping off a cliff.

One of the photographers behind the goal said, 'There's ten minutes, Ronnie.' I know he was trying to be helpful, but he just made it worse. So near but yet so far. All of a sudden Howard Kendall came through on a one-two with Alan Ball. It was a ball I'd normally have dived on, but the thigh had slowed me up so much, I was glad to block it with my legs.

The photographer said, 'Five minutes,' and I don't know which was worse, the pain in my thigh or the feeling I'd got in my stomach. At the other end, Danny put in a tremendous volley that Rankin turned over the top. They cleared the corner; and they came away. I could feel that this was it, that they were going to get through, and it was going to be left to me. More than that, I knew it was going to be the kind of save I dreaded making.

Bally came sprinting through with it, went round Graham Gibbs, dummied to go right for a shot, then slipped it left, for Joe Royle.

Royle came in and hit it first time from about fifteen yards, along the ground, to my right-hand corner, and at that moment, I didn't even think about it, I just threw myself. I got my hand to the ball; next thing I hit the ground, it was like my thigh had caught fire; and out I went.

When I came round, Don was giving me the smelling

salts. I grabbed him by his tracksuit, I said, 'What happened, Don? What happened? Did I save it?'

He said, 'Listen,' and I listened. Behind the goal, the Borough supporters were singing, 'We've won the Cup! We've won the Cup!'

'All you've got to do is clear the corner,' he said.

'Me?' I said. 'I could clear fifty corners.'